the world of automobiles

An Illustrated Encyclopedia of the Motor Car

COLUMBIA HOUSE/New York

Executive Editor: Ian Ward
Editorial Director: Brian Innes
Assistant Editors: Laurie Caddell
Mike Winfield
Charles Merullo
Art Editor: David Goodman
Art Assistant: John Heritage
Picture Editor: Mirco Decet
Cover Design: Harry W. Fass
Production Manager: Warren Bright

contributors
DAVID BURGESS WISE:
Swift
Talbot
Taxi-Cab
Thomas
Thomas-Flyer
Thornycroft
Trojan
Tucker
Turcat-Méry
Turner
EDWARD FRANCIS:
Tatra
Traffic Engineering
Trident
Triumph
BRYAN JONES: Toyota
MIKE KETTLEWELL: Targa Florio
Taruffi
Tasman Cup
Tecno
Thompson
Toivonen
Tourist Trophy
Trana
Trintignant
Trips
TVR

CLIVE RICHARDSON: Trials
L. J. K. SETRIGHT: Tojeiro
Transmission
DAVID VIZARD:
Tuning and Modification
IAN WARD: Torque
WORDSMITHS LTD:
Synchromesh
Tachometer
Tappets
Temperature Gauge
Tools

Picture acknowledgments
Page 2281: ICP—2282: National Magazine
Company; National Motor Museum; Marka
—2282-3: National Motor Museum—2283:
National Motor Museum; G. Goddard—
2285: Carpinacci; Quattroruote; Quat-
troruote—2286: AC-Delco; Papetti; I.
Ward/Orbis—2287: Smiths; Smiths; P.
Revere—2288: Belli; C. Burgess Wise;
National Motor Museum—2289: National
Motor Museum—2290: Belli; 2291: Belli;
National Motor Museum—2292: Belli—
2294: Papetti—2295: Quattroruote—
2296: Quattroruote—2297: Quattroruote—
2298: G. Goddard—2299: Quattroruote;
Quattroruote; G. Goddard—2300:
G. Goddard; A. Morland; A. Morland—
2301: C. Posthumus; Quattroruote—2302:
M. Kettlewell; London Art Tech—2302-3:
Quattroruote—2304: M. Kettlewell—
2304-5: M. Kettlewell—2306: Belli—
2307: Belli; National Motor Museum; Belli
—2308: National Motor Museum—2308-9:
Quattroruote—2310: Belli; Quattroruote;
Quattroruote—2311: L. J. Caddell/Orbis;
Camera Press—2312: L. J. Caddell—2313:
Camera Press—2314: Camera Press—
2315: Keystone—2316: Zagari—2316-7:
Belli—2317: Zagari—2318: Attualfoto—
2319: Smiths Industries; AC-Delco; AC-
Delco—2320: I. Ward/Orbis—2321: W.
Boddy—2322: N. Bruce—2323: C. Burgess
Wise—2324: Harrah's Motor Museum—
2325: J. G. Rettie; C. Posthumus—2326:
National Motor Museum—2327: London Art
Tech—2328-9: National Motor Museum—
2330: National Motor Museum; National
Motor Museum; G. Gauld—2331: Fiat—
2332: Quattroruote; James Neill Ltd; Ceci
—2333: Abingdon King Dick Ltd—2334:
Ceci; M. Mole & Sons Ltd—2335: Marka—
2337: London Art Tech—2338: C. Posthumus—2339: C. Posthumus—2340: London Art Tech—2341: Toyota—2342:
Toyota—2343: Toyota—2344: Toyota—
2345: Toyota—2346: Toyota—2347:
Toyota—2349: L. J. Caddell/Orbis; Toyota
GB—2350: Quattroruote—2351: Mairani—
2352: Marka—2353: BIPS—2354: L. J.
Caddell/Orbis—2355: Saab—2356: Fiat—
2357: Valeo; Quattroruote; Quattroruote—
2358: Quattroruote; ZF; Quattroruote—
2359: Ford—2360: Quattroruote; Audi—
2361: A. Morland—2362: C. Taylor; A.
Morland; C. Taylor—2363: A. Morland—
2364: C. Taylor—2365: C. Taylor—2366:
Quattroruote—2367: National Motor Museum—2368: M. Kettlewell; Quattroruote—
2369: London Art Tech; G. Gauld—2370:
Rover-Triumph; Cherret; Quattroruote; Rover-Triumph—2372: J. Spencer
Smith; Rover-Triumph; Quattroruote—
2373: Boschetti; Quattroruote—2374:
Quattroruote; C. Pocklington—2375: Quattroruote—2376: Quattroruote—2377: Quattroruote—2378: C. Pocklington—2379: L. J.
Caddell/Orbis—2380: L. J. Caddell/Orbis
—2381: National Motor Museum—2382:
National Motor Museum—2383: National
Motor Museum; Trojan—2384: I. Ward—
2385: W. A. C. Pettit—2386: Automobile
Quarterly—2387: J. G. Rettie; D. Vizard—
2388: D. Vizard; Papetti—2388-9: Quattro-
ruote—2389: Quattroruote; D. Vizard; D.
Vizard—2390: Papetti; D. Vizard—2391:
Papetti; Papetti; Papetti; D. Vizard; D.
Vizard—2392: Papetti; Papetti; Papetti;
L. J. Caddell—2393: National Motor Mu-
seum—2394: National Motor Museum—
2395: National Motor Museum—2396:
National Motor Museum—2397: L. J.
Caddell/Orbis—2398: L. J. Caddell/Orbis;
C. Pocklington—2399: C. Pocklington; M.
Lilley—2400: L. J. Caddell/Orbis—cover:
W. A. C. Pettit; Automobile Quarterly

Distributed by Columbia House, 51 West 52nd Street, New York, New York 10019
Printed in U.S.A.

Contents

A RIVAL FOR AUSTIN & MORRIS

Swift was best known for its nimble and neat small cars which, during the early days of the company, enjoyed great success

THE SWIFT MOTOR COMPANY of Coventry could justifiably claim to be Britain's oldest manufacturer of self-propelled vehicles. Since 1869, as the European Sewing Machine Company (makers of the Swiftsure sewing machines), had been supplementing its 'Swiftsure Sewing Machines' with the first English 'boneshaker' velocipedes. To cover its new range of activities the firm's name was soon altered to Coventry Machinists' Company, and in 1870 they built the very first high wheeled 'ordinary' or 'penny farthing' bicycle to the designs of James Starley, the 'father of the cycle industry'.

Though Swift became one of the leading manufacturers of bicycles, they were late to enter the motor car field. When they did, in 1902, it was with a very unhappily designed vehicle. The unlovely *voiturette* was powered by a $4\frac{1}{2}$ hp single-cylinder engine of the De Dion type supplied by the Motor Manufacturing Company. The gear change was distinctly novel, with two sets of teeth on the crown wheel and two pinions, the choice of gear ratio being determined by dog clutches. To start this mechanical melange the hapless driver had to insert the crankhandle into a hole on the (unsprung) rear axle. The car was as unreliable as its specifications suggested, and it was not long before a more orthodox single cylinder Swift appeared, to be joined by a 10 hp model with a Swift-built twin-cylinder engine in 1904.

Subsequently, three- and four-cylinder models were added to the range, and the marque began to score successes in the major reliability trials of the day. In 1903 a Swift took a silver medal in the RAC Thousand Mile Reliability Trial, in their 1904 600-mile event a Swift was awarded a gold medal. In 1905 one of the new four-cylinder 16/20 hp Swifts competed for the RAC Tourist Trophy. It made an impressive non-stop run achieving the lowest petrol consumption of any of the four-cylinder vehicles in the competition at $26\frac{1}{2}$ miles per gallon. The following year, a Swift beat all-comers in the South Indian Official Reliability Trials, achieving maximum marks in all categories of the event—reliability, speed on hills, ease of control, petrol consumption and engine power—and was awarded the India Cup.

In the Scottish Trials that year another Swift swept the board, winning a gold medal for achieving $995\frac{1}{2}$ marks out of a possible 1000, a figure well ahead of any other car in the trials, irrespective of price, class or horse-power, and recording a fuel consumption of 36.04 mpg.

In 1907 a Swift again won a gold medal in the Scottish Trials; the marque also received a gold medal and the highest possible marks for its performance in the Irish Reliability Trials.

It might seem difficult to improve on these performances, but in 1908 Swift did just that, taking 999.2

Below: a 1903 four-seater Swift tourer; it was powered by a four-cylinder motor which developed 50 hp

marks out of 1000 in the Scottish Reliability Trials, making it three golds in a row in this event, which Swift claimed as the 'world's record for reliability'. A team of three Swifts was entered for the Irish Reliability Trials and triumphantly carried off three gold medals, the team challenge cup, and 2548 marks out of a possible 2550, a fine performance, indeed.

At that point Swift wisely decided to quit while they were still ahead of the game, commenting: 'When in 1908 Swifts secured the Scottish Trials Gold Medal for the third year in succession, the "Daily News" remarked, "The Swift might retire now and give someone else a chance." We took this advice for 1909 (especially as we had in as many orders as we could execute), and it is worthy of note that, although the climatic conditions were vastly improved, no car in the 1909 trials, irrespective of class, price, or horse-power, was able to approach the 1908 record of the 10-12 hp Swift.'

In 1909, the company announced 'a *good* small car', a 7 hp single-cylinder, also marketed by the Austin

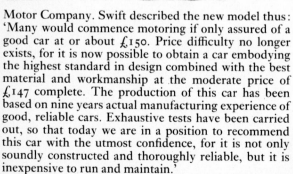

Motor Company. Swift described the new model thus: 'Many would commence motoring if only assured of a good car at or about £150. Price difficulty no longer exists, for it is now possible to obtain a car embodying the highest standard in design combined with the best material and workmanship at the moderate price of £147 complete. The production of this car has been based on nine years actual manufacturing experience of good, reliable cars. Exhaustive tests have been carried out, so that today we are in a position to recommend this car with the utmost confidence, for it is not only soundly constructed and thoroughly reliable, but it is inexpensive to run and maintain.'

However, even by the standards of 1910, the little Swift was totally outdated from the start, for the motoring public had been educated to expect something more refined from a light car than a badly balanced single-cylinder engine of 1100 cc and the good small car was out of production within a couple of years.

Also included in the 1910 range were the 10/12 hp two-cylinder 1814 cc, which was claimed to be 'admirably suited to a doctor's requirements . . . a large percentage of the total output of this type of car has passed into the hands of the medical profession, and letters are continually being received testifying to the all-round excellence of this type of vehicle as ideal for medical work.' A long wheel-base version of this car could carry a four-seater touring body. Then there was the 2315 cc 15/18 hp model, 'a handsomely appointed

Top: a 1910 single-seater Swift 7 hp

Above: the original Swift of 1902

Below: 1913 Swift runabout

first class four-cylinder touring car' and the 3628 cc 18/24 hp, 'a luxuriously appointed car, embracing all that is best in a high-class powerful touring vehicle'. There was also a low-geared, long-wheelbase version of this model, 'a splendid car for town use, specially adapted for town and theatre work'.

By 1913 the model line up had become even more complex, when the Swift company announced: 'The one thing that was needed to complete Motor History.' This was the 972 cc vertical twin cyclecar launched at the 1912 Motor Cycle and Cyclecar Show at Olympia. This model, which definitely did not make motoring history, became the smallest of a range otherwise consisting of a 1327 cc 10 hp, a 1795 cc 11.9 hp, a 1945 cc 14 hp, a 2614 cc 15.9 hp and a 3054 cc 20 hp, a wide range, indeed.

Only the 12 survived the war, and that for only a short while; it was joined at the 1919 Motor Show by an updated version of the 10 hp model.

The Swift cars of the 1920s were uniformly four-cylindered, thoroughly conservative in design and unremarkable in terms of power output. The specification of the 10 was mildly updated in 1923, when the engine acquired a detachable cylinder head and a gearbox built in unit. For 1926, the 1097 cc ten and the 12/35 hp, of 1954 cc, acquired four-wheel brakes; the following year, presumably to justify the fitting of all round retardation to cope with its somewhat lethargic performance, the 12/35 was uprated to the more fashionably middle class horsepower rating of 14/40, though engine design and capacity were unchanged.

By the end of the decade the 'sturdy ten' was the backbone of Swift production, which probably never exceeded 2000 units a year at its peak. At the end of 1928 a novel body style was offered on the 10 hp chassis. The Migrant sun or shade saloon, which at a price of £270 offered *two* sunshine roofs, one for the front seats, one for the back, both of which could be rolled back independently.

Below: a splendidly restored Swift 14/40 tourer of 1926

For 1930, the Ten was once again modernised with a narrow shell ribbon radiator and four-speed gear-box, a specification which was further improved for 1931 with a rear-mounted petrol tank, hydraulic shock absorbers, big-hub wire wheels, dipping headlamps a central chrome bar on the radiator shell and a new type of flush fitting sliding roof.

More traditional was the Ten's retention of right-hand gear change. Prices ranged from £250 for the three-seater drop-head coupé and the Nomad saloon to £295 for the Fleetwing fabric saloon on a specially tuned chassis.

Swift were losing out against mass producers like Morris and Austin who could afford to keep prices down as a result of large scale production; and they made the mistake of trying to fight the big battalions in a price war.

At the 1930 Olympia Motor Show came the announcement of a new 847 cc model, 'the Aristocrat of the Small Car World, the Swift Cadet—a car of individuality, taste and distinction—of limitless usefulness and enjoyment—and withal a moderate price.'

But at £160 the open tourer version of the Cadet was £20 more expensive than a coachbuilt saloon on the Morris Minor chassis of identical engine size, while the Cadet saloon, at £185, was definitely over-priced. The Cadet was certainly not the car to revive the flagging fortunes of Swift which continued to fail until, in 1932, the marque was dead. DBW

Left centre: a 1910 Swift 15/18 with coachwork by Maythorn

Bottom left: a Swift tourer pictured at a gathering of vintage and veteran cars

GEAR CHANGING MADE EASY

Since the introduction of synchromesh, much of the drudge and misery has been taken out of changing gear in a motor car

Left: a section of a modern four-speed all-synchromesh gearbox, showing the externally toothed synchromesh baulk rings between the gears of the mainshaft cluster

A BASIC GEARBOX consists of a number of gearwheels, which transmit power from one shaft to another; by selection of the correct size of gearwheel, the required shaft speed can be obtained. In changing gear, the gearwheels are moved so that combinations of different-sized gearwheels come into mesh.

At one time, cars were fitted with the now-obsolete crash gearbox. In this, the gearwheels simply slid along splines into mesh. The disadvantage of this type of gearbox was that, for a silent gear-change, the gears had to be turning at the same speeds; thus, the driver, having disengaged one gear, had to release the clutch pedal and flip the accelerator to rev the engine to the speed at which it would have been running if the required gears had been in mesh. The driver had to declutch again and the gears were left rotating at the correct speed under their own impetus. They then slid into mesh quietly and easily.

This method of gear-changing is known as 'double declutching'. If the driver failed to double declutch correctly, the gears grated, excessive wear occurred and the gears may even have been damaged. Double declutching requires considerable skill and practice before it can be performed easily and effectively; although it is employed by some who regard driving and its techniques as an art, it is not now widely practised.

To overcome this disadvantage of the crash box, a system of automatic synchronisation of the gear speeds has been developed. The system, known as synchromesh, originated in America, where it appeared on Cadillac and La Salle cars in 1928. Vauxhall introduced it to the British motoring public in 1931.

These cars usually had only three gears and the synchromesh was fitted only between second and top gear. Four-speed gear boxes had synchromesh on second, third and top gears. Most modern cars now have synchromesh on all forward gears, regardless of the number, while reverse gears are not normally fitted with this device.

Several types of synchromesh are in common use. The constant load synchroniser is one of the oldest types still in use. It operates by means of two conical surfaces, whose engagement is caused by the gear-change; the friction of the surfaces brings the rotating parts to a similar speed. Another member is also moved but delayed by a spring loading arrangement. This component is toothed, the teeth positively engaging the two rotating parts.

Another type of synchromesh, of more recent design, is the baulk-ring type. This employs a baulk ring that prevents the gears' engaging before they are rotating at the correct speeds. A particularly interesting baulk-ring type is the Porsche system. It is based on a minimum number of components and, additionally, lightens the gear-change movement by a servo action.

The basis of the Porsche synchromesh system is a circular clutch unit with internal teeth. The teeth are

Above: the idea of synchromesh is to encourage the separate parts of a gearbox to rotate at equal speeds, in order to allow silent engagement of gears; two conical surfaces are brought together, the friction between them causing the speeds to synchronise, as shown on the right

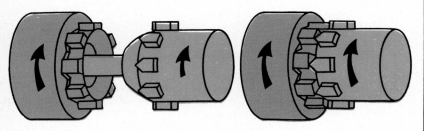

Above: in practice, the outer surfaces of the shafts are splined, one side carrying an internally splined collar; when the speeds have been synchronised by the cones, the splines may still not be aligned, so those on the collarless side are pointed to facilitate engagement

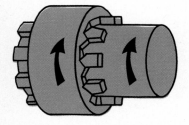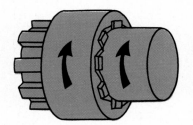

Above: as the collar slides along the shaft, it engages with the pointed splines, aligning them as it does so, and locks the two shafts together; in the more effective baulk-ring system, an intermediate ring prevents engagement of the gears before speeds have been synchronised

chamfered so that, when the unit is shifted by the forked gear-change lever, they contact a chamfered split ring, which forms part of the gear to be engaged. Friction of the clutch unit against the chamfered split ring causes the gear assembly to rotate at the same speed as the clutch unit. Further movement of the gear lever

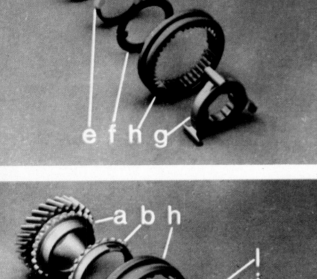

Left: exploded views of three different types of baulk-ring synchromesh unit, ie sprung-ring, free-ring and reversed-cone; the letter b, in red, represents the baulk ring in each case; the other parts are as follows:
a gear
c thrust ring
d thrust peg
e braking peg
f sprung ring
g hub splined to shaft
h sliding collar
i spring
l pegs
m spring-support ring
n spring

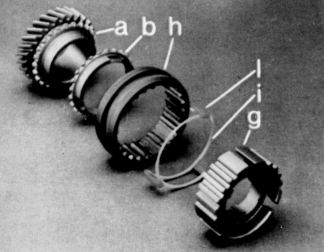

brings the teeth of the clutch unit into engagement with teeth on the end of the gear assembly, thereby achieving the final positive engagement.

The synchronising components of this system are extremely compact: full synchromesh gearboxes can be built, no larger than the old-fashioned crash boxes.

A wide variety of synchromesh systems, developed from the original idea, are now in existence. Most manufacturers have their own variations to suit their particular requirements. They all rely for their operation, however, on the effects of friction to rotate the gearbox components at the correct speed for engagement of the chosen gears.

One variant of the original idea uses lozenge-shaped blocks, which baulk any gear-meshing until the correct speed has been obtained. Another method uses spring split rings, which spring outwards and contact an external ring on the gear assembly. They bear on this and rotate it until the rotational speeds are identical, at which time the outward pressure will cease and the spring will fall back, so allowing the gears to engage.

A means of changing gears without either double declutching or the use of a synchromesh system is available with the freewheel device fitted to some pre-1960 cars. This freewheel system allows the gearbox and engine to return to idling speed when the car is not being 'driven'. Thus, gears may be disengaged and engaged without the use of either the clutch or synchromesh. By just removing his foot from the accelerator, the driver can achieve completely smooth and noiseless gear changes.

The Warren synchroniser, a device no longer in general use, is fitted between the gearbox and the propeller shaft and is operated by the clutch pedal. When the driver disconnects the gearbox from the engine, the Warren synchroniser disconnects the gearbox from the propeller shaft and the driving wheels. This allows the gears to stop rotating completely and the gearchange can be made quickly and easily. When the driver accelerates, the synchroniser resumes transmission of power to the propeller shaft and the driving wheels.

A useful advantage of the Warren synchroniser was that it could be used as a freewheel device. The driver, by depressing and releasing the clutch, disconnected the drive until he accelerated and the drive connected again automatically.

After a long working life, the synchromesh components of a gearbox will become worn. This will lead to a tendency for the driver to over-ride the synchromesh and to engage the gears before they are rotating at the correct speed. This is a noisy operation and it causes excessive wear on the gear teeth.

If synchromesh components do become ineffective for this reason, the only means of rectifying the situation is to replace the worn parts. If the gear changes are not rushed, however, the system may well operate satisfactorily. If it does deteriorate to the point where it becomes virtually inoperative, the driver can always resort to double declutching, rather than invest in an expensive repair to what is probably an already ageing car.

One possible danger is the addition of lubricating additives to the gearbox oil. These, while possibly reducing the effects of friction and wear on the gears and bearings, may reduce also the frictional effects on which the synchromesh system depends for its operation. If a gearbox has become noisy as a result of old age, it may be more prudent to consider a different grade of oil—or if ordinary engine oil is specified, to use a hypoid oil—than to run the risk of reducing the effectiveness of an already worn unit. NHP-G

RUNNING INTO THE RED

The tachometer, or rev counter, is one of the most important instruments on a car, yet many manufacturers still do not fit them as standard items

Above: an early tachometer from Jaeger of France

Above right: back and front views of a modern Veglia electronic tachometer

Right: a pair of tachometers by Time Instruments, one for panel mounting and one, with a cowl, for affixing to the top of the dash; note that both instruments have adjustable red-lines, to indicate the particular vehicle's rev limit

THE TACHOMETER, or revolution counter, is an instrument for measuring the speed of rotation particularly of a vehicle's engine; the road speed of a vehicle is measured by the speedometer. Unlike the speedometer, the tachometer is not a legal requirement and is usually confined to sports, high-performance and the more expensive range of cars. It is, however, a most useful instrument, and is easily fitted to any vehicle.

Early models of tachometers depended on a geared rotating mechanical drive taken from some moving part of the engine, such as the flywheel, camshaft, fan pulley, etc. The drive rotated a magnet, thus inducing eddy currents in an aluminium disc, much like a speedometer, but the scale was, of course, marked in revolutions per minute. Modern car tachometers are almost always electronic, operated by impulse from the low-tension 'make and break' of the distributor points.

The Smith's Industries instrument is a good example of the latest impulse tachometer. Two pairs of connections are required, one pair for the supply leads and the other for the pulse pick-up leads. The pulse leads are, in fact, one continuous wire with a loop (forming the primary winding of a transformer) taken around a soft iron core projecting from the rear of the tachometer casing. The advantages of this type of signal pick-up are that there is no break in the ignition wiring, so a break in the tachometer circuit will not affect the ignition; and that there is no direct electrical connection to the ignition from the tachometer circuit. The secondary of the transformer, inside the tachometer case, is connected to a printed circuit that applies current pulses, originating from the distributor and therefore at a frequency depending on engine speed, to the indicating meter. The internal circuit is fed from the supply leads, one of which is taken to one of the vehicle's existing switched and fused circuits running back to the battery, the other to earth (ground). Of the pulse leads, one is

taken to the contact breaker (CB) terminal on the ignition coil, the other to the contact breaker (side) terminal on the distributor. The previously existing CB to distributor wiring is discarded. Note, however, that on some modern ignition coils, the SW and CB connections are now marked '−' and '+' for positive earth systems and '+' and '−' for negative earth systems. If a radio is fitted to the car, the CB to distributor wire may be a noise suppressor lead; if this is so, do not remove it, but instead, disconnect the wire leading to the SW terminal of the coil and connect the pulse coil of the tachometer between the end of this lead and the SW terminal.

On some models of tachometer, separate leads are provided for internal illumination and must be taken to an existing lighting circuit. Fitting is well within the scope of the average motoring enthusiast and motor accessory shops usually have a range of tachometers available. There are separate 4 and 6-cylinder models

Above left: an auxiliary instrument panel, from Smiths, carrying a vacuum gauge, an ammeter and an electronic tachometer

Above: various types of scale have been tried for tachometers; the 'normal' circular dial has been the most popular, but rotating drum and ribbon models have also been tried

Left: a Smiths unit, with the paraphernalia necessary for mounting and connection

(suitable also for 2- and 3-cylinder 2-stroke engines respectively). Make sure that the voltage and polarity (positive or negative) matches that of the car. Full fitting instructions are provided and must be carefully followed; a support or accessory panel can be used for mounting the instrument above or below the fascia.

One of the main uses of the tachometer is assisting the driver in correctly relating engine speed to road speed, so that gears can be changed at the optimum combination of these two factors, achieving the best power/speed ratio and the most economical use of fuel. Thus, ideally, the engine speed will, as far as possible, be held, through the gears, within the range 2,000 to 3,000 revs/min (r.p.m.). Variations of these limits are of course possible, depending on the particular car; some manufacturers mark the tachometer with coloured segments related to the gear engaged. Although the tachometer is usually calibrated up to 8,000 or 10,000 revs/min., the maximum permissible speed for most engines is usually well below this figure. Some tachometers are provided with a red 'do not enter' segment; others have an adjustable red pointer to indicate the limit; but on no account should the manufacturer's recommended maximum speed be exceeded.

When the engine is tuned, the distributor points must be set to open a certain number of degrees before TDC (top dead centre). Most manufacturers lay down the engine speed, or narrow range of speeds, at which this setting must, for maximum effectiveness, be under-taken. A common speed is 800 revs/min., but some makers lay down 1,700 or even 3,000 revs/min. It is clearly not possible to attain these engine speeds accurately without a tachometer. For small carburettor or distributor gap changes, the tachometer is far more sensitive than the vacuum gauge.

If it appears that full power is not being obtained, perhaps due to a sticking valve, defective piston ring or faulty sparking plug, the faulty cylinder can immediately be determined by shorting each plug to earth—taking care to grasp only the insulated handle of the screwdriver used for the purpose. The loss of each cylinder, as it is short-circuited, should produce exactly the same loss in revs/min; if the loss of any one cylinder shows a smaller dip on the tachometer pointer than the others, that one cylinder must be assumed to be defective in some way.

On diesel engines, which have no ignition system, the impulse tachometer cannot be used, but other types are available; for example, an insulated extension shaft, set with soft iron bars. Magnets or energized coils surround the shaft and more or less current is generated in proportion to the engine speed. This type of ac generator may operate a dc moving coil type of meter through a rectifier, or it may drive a remote motor which in turn operates a mechanically driven instrument. Pulse generators, similar to a small ignition coil and having a mechanical or magnetic drive, are an alternative to the ac generator type. AGH

A JUNGLE OF CONFUSION

The Talbot story could easily rival an Agatha Christie novel for its complex twists and turns of fate

Above: a 1914 Talbot advertising picture

Right: a 1906 Talbot tourer competing in a recent Vintage Car Club get-together

IT IS A SURE BET that any early motoring concern connected with M. Adolphe Clément was never a straight forward and uncomplicated affair; but the Talbot history, even though M. Clément dropped out of the scene at an early stage, was particularly convoluted.

At the turn of the century, Clément cars were imported into England by Danny Weigel, whose business associate, the wealthy Earl of Shrewsbury and Talbot, had ambitions to produce a quality car. Adolphe Clément was never adverse to taking money from the mighty, and so the Clement Talbot company was founded on October 11, 1902, and work began on a splendid terra-cotta factory on a five-acre site in what was to become Barlby Road, Ladbroke Grove, North Kensington. While work was in hand, Clément cars were imported from France and sold as Clement Talbots (in their home country they were now known as Clément-Bayards). By the end of 1904 the British cars were simply called Talbots. However, at the same time French built Clément-Gladiators were being imported by one E. H. Lancaster, and after 1908 the Clement name appeared on cars built in the Swift factory, fitted with radiators of similar design to the British Talbot and marketed under the slogan 'simply Clement, nothing else'. These British Clements did not survive the outbreak of war.

Meanwhile, back in Ladbroke Grove, the new factory had begun assembly, and partial production, of French designed cars. At the 1905 Automobile Show at the Crystal Palace from January 27–February 4, the 'Great National Firm' exhibited an impressive line-up of cars: four twin-cylinder models, the 7/8 hp 2 V, the 8/9 hp 2 VB, the 9/11 hp 2 K and the 10/12 hp 2 O; and

five four-cylinder models, 12/14 hp 4 V, the 12/16 hp 4 VB, the 16/20 hp 4 K, the 24/30 hp 4 X and the 35/50 hp 4 Y, the latter being a 6.3-litre car retailing at £820 in chassis form.

The first all-British Talbot appeared in 1906, the 3780 cc 20/24 hp designed by C. R. Garrard, the works manager. Both this car and the 2724 cc 12/16 hp established themselves as notable performers in hill-climbs and speed trials, even as far afield as Australia where the company had early established an export market. At the 1906 Olympia Show a new British Talbot model was introduced, the 2977 cc 15 hp which supplanted the 12/16, and which featured dual high-tension ignition with automatic advance.

During 1907, the marque recorded 109 victories in hill-climbs and speed contests, including a 'world record for efficiency' at the Caerphilly hill-climb.

The 1908 range was a judicious mixture of French and English models, from a 8/10 hp 2-cylinder to a monstrous 8621 cc four-cylinder 50/60 hp model with a chassis price of £1000; included were two uncharacteristic models, a 12 hp and a 35/45 hp, both with chain drive, whereas the majority of Talbot cars had live rear axles. Also new was a 4156 cc 25 hp which lasted in production until 1910.

By now the marque's sporting successes had earned it the slogan of 'the Invincible Talbot'. The 1908 models had introduced L-head cylinder blocks in place of the less efficient T-head, but these designs were not to realise their full potential until in 1911 the company acquired a new chief engineer, G. W. A. Brown, who had previously worked for Austin.

Among Brown's achievements had been the development of a remarkable series of Austin racing cars called *Pearley* for the racing driver Percy Lambert; and now George Brown was to apply the same skill to the 25 hp Talbot engine, which had already been redesigned for 1910 to give a swept volume of 4487 cc. Brown succeeded in doubling the power output of the Talbot engine, and a pair of ultra streamlined racing and sprint cars was built for Percy Lambert and Leslie Hands. Lambert first appeared with this car at Brooklands at Motor Show time, 1912, setting up a string of records which all but eclipsed the earlier Sunbeam victory in the Coupe de l'Auto causing the motoring journalist Wilfred Gordon Aston to comment: 'Another British firm has put up another extraordinary performance, and one that it is not too much to say has electrified the whole motor industry and left it still wondering and gaping for all the world as though a comet had suddenly flashed past its eyes. . . . On November 16, a 25 hp Talbot of standard dimensions and standard design, but of course with the modifications required for racing work, set up the following records: the half mile at 113.28 mph; the mile at 111.73 mph and the 2¾ miles lap at 109.43 mph. It is needless to attempt to smother this performance with superlatives, for it is neither more nor less than staggering. No one need have any difficulty in predicting that these figures will stand for a very great length of time especially when one considers that they have only been beaten by cars of at least three times the engine size. Some may say, "After all, mere racing proves nothing beyond the fact that a special car can do a special performance", but past experience shows them to be utterly wrong. Racing is *the* one and only training school for the development and perfection of the touring car. The man who can make the fastest car is the man who can make the best car, and as far as the invincible Talbot is concerned—well, there are the figures.'

On February 15, 1913, Percy Lambert covered 103.76 miles in an hour at Brooklands, thus becoming the first man ever to cover 100 miles in 60 minutes. Though the Talbot records were soon broken, it was by racing monsters of two and three times the engine power, whereas the Talbot was basically a standard 25 hp chassis. The company made much of Lambert's achievement: 'A car that can survive this phenomenal ordeal will take you up the stiffest hills without faltering, and reveal an enduring disregard for arduous service.'

Nor was the 100 miles in the hour the sum total of the Talbot's capabilities for it was also successful in speed trials, yet was tractable enough to be driven on the public road. Top speed of the car was over 120 mph and it may have been this speed capability which led Lambert to fit a 4¾-litre engine to the car in order to recapture his record. In any case this was to be his last season of racing, as he had recently become engaged

and had promised his fiancée that he would give up record breaking. His last attempt to recapture the hour's record was made on Friday, October 31, 1913, and the Talbot was lapping at around 110 mph when a rear tyre burst. The car flew out of control and crashed, killing Lambert. Five days later he was buried in Brompton Cemetery in a coffin streamlined to match his car; the remains of the Talbot were acquired by G. A. 'Tony' Vandervell, who incorporated them in a postwar Brooklands racer, while the sister car was driven in the 1920s by Malcolm Campbell.

With the outbreak of war, George Brown left Talbot; he was replaced in 1916 by a young Swiss engineer

Below: a view of the machine shop of the Clément Talbot motor works, taken in 1912

Above: a gathering of 1½-litre Grand Prix Talbot Darracqs at a race meeting held during 1926

named Georges Roesch, who had previously worked with Gregoire Delaunay Belleville, where he received much useful instruction from Marius Barbaroux, at Renault and at Daimler of Coventry. Roesch's brief was to develop a car for production after the Armistice and he devised a remarkable 1750 cc model called the Talbot A 12 which was full of novel features such as a pressed steel box under the front seats which also acted as storage for the spare wheel and tool box, as a cross member for the chassis and as running boards and attachment points for the mudguards. The two/three seat bodywork ended in a rounded stern with a luggage carrier formed between the rear dumb-irons; many of the features of this car were patented, and a prototype was built but the model was destined never to reach production status. The Earl of Shrewsbury's only son had been killed on the Western Front, and the Earl was no longer interested in the company he had founded. At that period the Société Alexandre Darracq, a French-based, British-capitalised, company was in an expansive mood and began making overtures to Talbot, which were accepted in 1919. The ink was scarcely dry on the contract before Darracq amalgamated with Sunbeam of Wolverhampton, creating the Sunbeam-Talbot-Darracq group. Heading the STD combine was the Breton engineer, Louis Coatalen. He decided to drop the Talbot A12 in favour of new designs by Owen Clegg of Darracq. Less comprehensible was the decision to amend the Darracq name and call the cars built at the Suresnes, Paris factory, Talbot-Darracq.

After Sunbeam joined the group the Parisian cars were called simply Talbots (with a French accent); to avoid confusion between the cars from Ladbroke Grove, and those from Suresnes. The French cars were sold on the English market as Talbot-Darracqs or Darracqs. This confusion of identities became yet more complicated when the STD group began building racing cars which, depending on where they were built and raced, were variously known as Talbot, Talbot-Darracq, Talbot Special or Sunbeam.

Initially, Coatalen plans for the Talbot factory were simple; while it geared itself up to produce a new utility car, it would be occupied in building three racing cars for the STD Combine. But this left the company up in the air with regard to producing vehicles for immediate needs; they had managed to keep a certain level of business in operation by buying back war-surplus Talbot ambulances and rebuilding them as touring cars. When the supply of ambulance chassis inevitably dried up they were forced to reintroduce their pre-war models as a stop gap until the arrival of the new small car. The first 8/18 hp Talbot was exhibited at the 1921 Motor Show, after which it went into production at Barlby Road; its 967 cc pushrod ohv power unit was the best part of the design, for the chassis was more suited to the long, straight Routes Nationales of France than to the rolling English road, and consequently Roesch had to redesign the car, increasing engine capacity to 1074 cc and lengthening the chassis to take full four-seater coachwork. Roesch's reconsideration of the

French Talbot, was termed the 10/23.

Incidentally, at this period the 8/18 was also assembled in the old Darracq coachbuilding works at Acton, and differed only from its English counterpart in the shape of its radiator.

Roesch spent a couple of frustrating years being shunted around the design offices of the STD combine during which time Clement-Talbot Limited virtually went out of business. Coatalen, suffering from ill health and unable to redeem the situation, which had been brought on by the fact that the 10/23 hp cost twice as much as most of its rivals, telegraphed to Roesch who was then working in the Suresnes factory and asked him to return to London and take over Talbot.

His task was unenviable; he had to produce a new design on outmoded machinery that dated back to the foundation of the company—and he had to do it before the company's dwindling bank credit ran out, which gave him only a matter of months. Roesch's goal was to produce a car which offered the excellence of the new Rolls Royce 20, with half the engine capacity, at a quarter the price. The new Talbot 14/45 which appeared in 1926 was a refined and well engineered car at a surprisingly low price; it used many of the proven features of the over-priced Paris-designed Talbot 12/30 Six in conjunction with brilliant ideas from Roesch, including his ingenious overhead pushrod layout which utilised ultra thin pushrods (which were in fact made by a company of knitting needle manufacturers) acting on light rockers pivoting on an overhead knife edge to reduce friction and weight.

The power unit, with a 1666 cc swept volume could turn at 4500 rpm, a revolution rate one third greater than its predecessor. Other advanced features of the design included a rigid, well-braced chassis and noiseless dynamotor starting (which was however to prove something of an Achilles heel on later models). Between the front and rear dumb irons were illuminated boxes incorporating directional arrow signals operated by a switch on the steering wheel, probably the first time an automatic signalling device had been incorporated in a production vehicle.

'With steering so delicate and light that two fingers

Right: a 14 hp Talbot M75 two-seater spider model of 1930; this is one of only two models of this type in existence. Its value is commensurate with its scarcity

on the wheel are as adequate at 60 mph as at 6 mph, a gear change which a child could operate effortlessly and noiselessly, a smooth clutch and good brakes, the longest, most difficult run is sheer pleasure from beginning to end,' enthused *The Motor* early in 1927, when production of the new car had already reached fifty a week. The 14/45 was a car capable of much development, and was to have the production life of almost a decade. Building on the same basic formula, Roesch introduced a new model in 1930 with a 2276 cc power unit capable of far greater performance. It was available in two guises, the 70 and the 90, designations which reflected the the top speed of the vehicles. Both were of similar design, though the 90 was on a short chassis and a raised compression ratio and larger carburetter priced at £675, in standard sporting four-seater form, it offered remarkable value for money compared, for example with the contemporary 2.9-litre Lagonda which was £945 in similar form.

Its unexciting looking power unit, with its plain exterior and single carburettor was extremely reliable yet almost uncannily silent, though its competition debut in the Brooklands Double-Twelve in May 1930 was marred by a tragic crash which eliminated two of the cars and resulted in the death of a mechanic and a spectator. But a few weeks later the cars, which were raced under the control of the motor dealers Fox and Nicholl, took third and fourth places at Le Mans, winning the performance index. Then came class wins in the Irish Grand Prix, the Ulster TT and the Brooklands 500 Mile Race.

In the Spring of 1931 came a new competition version of the Talbot, the 105 with a 2969 cc engine, developing 140 bhp in competition trim. However, this larger engine was almost too much for the direct drive dynamotor to cope with, and two 12-volt batteries had to be fitted for starting purposes. The potential of the new model was shown in the otherwise boring 1931 Double-Twelve, which was won on handicap by MG Midgets, for the team of Talbots covered a greater distance during the twenty-four hours than any other entrant, winning a hollow victory in the poorly contested 3-litre class.

Like all Roesch cars the 105 was outstandingly versatile; in order to secure a sale, a member of the Talbot staff on the stand at the 1932 Glasgow Motor Show, beat an express train back to London, averaging over 53 mph for more than 400 miles. Talbot 105s achieved high placings at Le Mans and in the Alpine Trials in 1931 and 32, as well as in the 1000 Miles Race at Brooklands (which replaced the double-twelve) and in the BRDC 500 Miles Race. But at the end of 1932, from a combination of financial and technical reasons, Clement-Talbot Limited decided to withdraw from competition and withdrew their backing from the Fox and Nicholl team.

Increasing weight necessitated an ultra-low back axle ration on the 1930s developments of the old 14/45, like the 1932 Talbot 65, which won the coachwork award in the RAC Rally but needed a final drive ratio of 5.875:1 to keep its unladen weight of 26 cwt on the move.

But nevertheless Talbots were still excellent value for money, and became even more so when prices were substantially reduced at the 1932 Motor Show. A new development of the 105, the long wheelbase 95, was announced for 1933 as well as a self-changing epicyclic gearbox of Wilson type built in the Talbot factory became available as an option, adding considerably to the starting problem of the already overworked dyna-motor, so that Roesch was compelled to develop an automatic centrifugal clutch which disconnected the engine from the transmission at idling speeds. Though the other two components of the STD combine were in financial trouble, Talbot appeared both technically and commercially to be at its peak but doom was at hand, in the form of a £500,000 note falling due on 30 September 1934 without the means to meet it. The Rootes Brothers, who five years earlier had refused to save Clyno, now took an active interest in the salvation

Below: a 2.3-litre Talbot M67C coupé model of 1930

Bottom: in 1935, Talbot produced this sports saloon known as the Talbot 75; it was powered by a 2276 cc, overhead-valve, six-cylinder engine

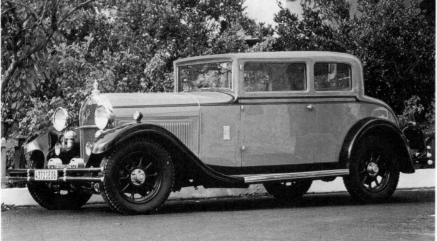

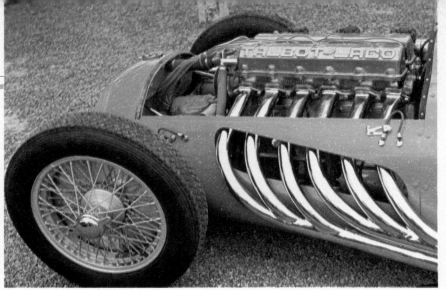

of the Sunbeam and Talbot companies (Coatalen had ensured that the French Talbot factory was free from any liability under the notes). Rootes had already acquired Humber and Hillman, and when in 1934 the STD creditors appointed a receiver, it was only a matter of months before Sunbeam and Talbot became part of the Rootes group. The Rootes Brothers were purveyors of pretty packages rather than automotive engineers, and they continued the Roesch models only so long as was necessary to use up the stock of existing parts. Meanwhile Roesch was compelled to supervise the development of a depressing 'Talbot Ten' based on the Hillman Aero Minx chassis, while the larger models were redesigned to follow the appearance of the new Ten. Increasingly, the big Talbots became more and more like the contemporary Humbers and Hillmans and at the 1937 Motor Show a new 'Talbot 3-litre' was announced, which was in fact a Hillman Hawk in Talbot clothing which could hardly reach 80 mph (though the press claimed, unbelievably that it was a better car than the old 105).

The Barlby Road factory had become little more than an assembly plant for Coventry-built components and at the end of 1938 the marque was renamed Sunbeam-Talbot under which guise it produced warmed-up versions of the staider Rootes models until 1954. Manufacture ceased at Barlby Road in 1945 when the company's headquarters were moved to Ryton-on-Dunsmore in Warwickshire. Roesch had resigned in 1938 to join the David Brown group as chief engineer of their tractor division in Huddersfield; he died in

November 1969, having seen the classic Talbots revived in vintage events while the Rootes monstrosities were consigned to a well deserved historical limbo.

As for the French connection of STD, after the group receivership, it had been taken over by Major Anthony Lago who had introduced a new model with a 3-litre engine in a Delahaye chassis; he continued to build cars under the Talbot and Lago-Talbot marque names at Suresnes until 1959 when the factory was taken over by Simca who killed off the Talbot name in 1960. So the S-T-D companies were eventually reunited under the Chrysler banner. . . .   DBW

Top: three views of the 1949 Talbot-Lago Grand Prix car, this was powered by a six-cylinder engine of 4.5 litres

Above: a Talbot-Lago Record of 1951. It was fitted with a detuned version of the engine used in the GP car

AN IMPORTANT PART OF THE VALVE TRAIN

The tappet is a small member interposed between each camshaft lobe and the valve-lifting mechanism, or the valve itself, depending on the design of the engine

THE TAPPET, known also as the cam follower or valve lifter, is a small member interposed between each camshaft lobe and the valve lifting mechanism, or the valve itself, depending on engine design.

'Valve lifting' means raising the valve off its seat. Only on side valve engines is the valve actually lifted upwards; overhead valves are actually depressed in order to 'lift' or open them.

As a camshaft rotates, each lobe produces both a vertical and a side thrust. The side thrust does no useful work and the purpose of the tappet is to eliminate it so that only vertical motion is transmitted to the push rod or valve.

The centre of the tappet is usually offset in relation to the cam—this is done so that the tappet is rotated slightly on each contact with the lobe, thus spreading tappet wear over a large area.

Tappets for conventional-camshaft engines are usually of cylindrical or mushroom shape, about one inch long, and are located in guides machined in the engine block. Sometimes, the inside of the tappet is partially hollowed out so that the push rod fits down inside it; in others, an adjustment screw and locknut is fitted to one end, the pushrod resting in a depression in the screw head. Lubrication is sometimes provided by spiral oil-retaining grooves, machines on the cylindrical face, but more often by oil mist or splashes, or by oil running down the push rod.

The automatically adjusting hydraulic tappet incorporates a spring-loaded plunger inside the main body. A cavity in the plunger is charged with oil through a ball valve. Initially, the spring expands the tappet to take up all the clearance in the valve train. As the cam lifts the valve, the ball valve closes, retaining the oil in the plunger. When the tip of the lobe has passed the tappet, the spring expands slightly, so that oil is drawn into the plunger cavity from that collected at the base of the push rod, the cavity thus being constantly replenished. When valve stem lengthens with normal heat expansion, the cavity is compressed slightly and surplus oil leaks out through the slight clearance around the circumference of the plunger.

Tappets for overhead camshafts take other forms: some are caps resting directly over the tops of the valve stems (with direct acting camshafts), while others are levers or 'fingers' (with indirect acting camshafts), hinged either at the centre or at one end, sometimes with a roller to actuate the valve.

All tappets are 'case hardened'; that is to say, a very hard surface layer is produced on them by heating in a carbonaceous medium. Case hardening enables the tappet to withstand the constant battering it receives, without risk of shattering.

When the engine is running, the valves become heated and the valve stems expand. A certain gap, or clearance, must therefore be provided in the valve operating train to accommodate this expansion, otherwise the valve will not close properly. On the other

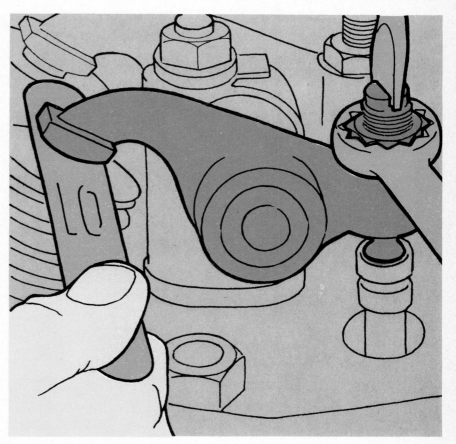

Above: in an engine with valves operated through pushrods and rockers, it is usual to adjust the tappets by means of spanner, screwdriver and feeler gauge

hand, excessive clearance reduces the valve lift and hence the period during which it is fully open. On older vehicles, valve clearances were generally less than today, being about 0.003 in (0.1 mm) for the inlet valves and 0.005 in (0.15 mm) for the exhaust. Frequent adjustment was necessary.

Today, intervals of 6,000 or even 10,000 miles between checks and adjustment are commonplace. Clearances are generally between 0.010 and 0.015 in (0.25 and 0.40 mm) for inlet valves and 0.012 and 0.018 in (0.30 and 0.45 mm) for the exhaust, although some manufacturers specify the same clearance for both inlet and exhaust valve mechanisms. The correct clearance for each valve can be set only when the relative cam is turned directly away from the tappet affected. If the camshaft is not visible, the correct cam positions can be found by taking note of the opening and closing of the valves; appropriate information will be found in the manufacturer's handbook.

Measurement of the clearance is made with a feeler gauge, inserted between the cam and tappet or the valve stem and its operating member. The clearance is correct when it is just possible to enter a gauge blade of the designated thickness between the gap. Some manufac-

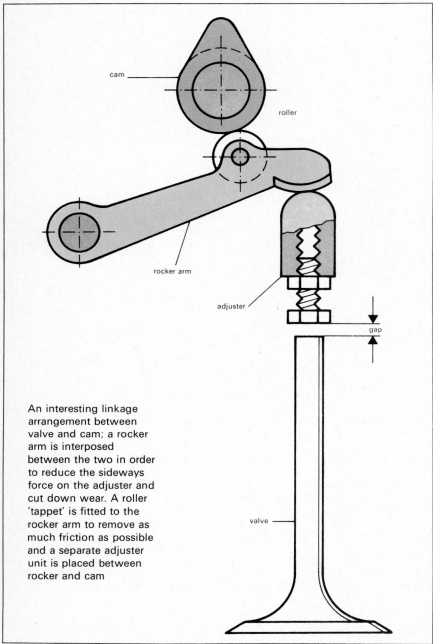

An interesting linkage arrangement between valve and cam; a rocker arm is interposed between the two in order to reduce the sideways force on the adjuster and cut down wear. A roller 'tappet' is fitted to the rocker arm to remove as much friction as possible and a separate adjuster unit is placed between rocker and cam

cam

roller

rocker arm

adjuster

gap

valve

Top: two types of tappet, both with adjusters built in; that on the right has a roller to reduce friction between itself and the cam

tappets or adjustable push rods. Always re-check the clearance after tightening the locknut, in case the set screw has moved. Another method is by a self-locking nut holding down the rocker arm at its centre against a spring; some manufacturers require the engine to be running when this type of operating mechanism is adjusted.

Sometimes shims or pads (known also as capsules) of varying thicknesses are incorporated into the valve operating train. The Jaguar, for example, uses a series of pads, lettered A to Z, rising in steps of 0.001 in from 0.85 in to 0.110 in. If, for instance, an inlet valve clearance measures 0.007 in, the correct clearance being 0.004 in, and the pad in place is lettered D, the clearance must be reduced by 0.003 in, therefore a 0.003 in thicker pad is required, lettered G. With this system, the pad is usually located in a shallow recess in the tappet and it may be necessary to compress the valve spring in order to remove and replace it.

Similar pad or shim systems are used by other manufacturers. On some overhead camshaft engines, the camshaft has to be removed before the pads can be changed. This necessitates the measuring and noting down of all of the clearances and the correct replacement pads before the camshaft is removed. On some Vauxhall overhead camshaft engines, the clearance is adjusted by a small socket head screw set in the side of the tappet—one complete turn varies the clearance by 0.003 in (0.08 mm).

When the engine is dismantled, the cam lobes and the cam face of each tappet should be carefully checked for wear. These parts, ideally, should be smooth and free from scores; the circumference of the tappets and the bore of their guides or housings should be perfectly round and an easy fit without sideplay. The cam face of each tappet will show whether the normal rotating or non-rotating wear pattern is present. The tappet may be excessively worn, but still in the case-hardened layer; or it may be 'soft worn', when this layer has been eroded away. If this softer metal is exposed, wear increases at a much faster rate and will already have become apparent by the necessity for frequent adjustment of the valve clearance.

With hydraulic tappets, the walls as well as the ends should be checked for wear and blowholes (which will result in oil leakage).

If more than 0.003 in (0.08 mm) side play in the tappet guides is present, the guide should be reamed out and an oversize tappet fitted.

Remember that if any part of the engine that affects the valve clearance is removed and subsequently replaced, 'bedding down' usually occurs necessitating a further tightening of securing nuts or screws. Such items include the cylinder head, rocker arm supports and overhead camshafts. It is essential to check, and adjust if necessary, the valve operating mechanism clearances, after this second tightening of these major components. AGH

turers provide a simple go/no go gauge in the tool kit—the 'go' gauge should pass easily between the gap, but the 'no go' gauge must not enter.

A common method of adjustment is by set screw and locknut; with a conventional camshaft and overhead valves, the screw is usually located in one end of each rocker arm. Side valve engines have either adjustable

Sicily's Classic

THE TARGA FLORIO was the world's last classic road race when it was run, ostensibly for the final time, in 1974 after having been held 54 previous times. Initiated in 1906, the year after the first RAC Tourist Trophy, it was second only to that race in its great age. In fact, for years devoted followers of the Sicilian event proudly boasted that their race preceded the first Grand Prix—if only by 50 days.

The Targa Florio was the idea of Vincenzo Florio, a member of one of the most wealthy families on the island of Sicily. By the time he was 21 Vincenzo Florio was a widely-travelled and sophisticated young man with experience in many sports, but passionately in love with the motor car.

Florio's first car was a De Dion Bouton tricycle, the first form of motorised transport on the island. Presently cars from Europe's leading manufacturers were purchased to form a large stable of machinery and Florio began to organise competitions, such as a speed test featuring his De Dion, a horse rider and a cyclist. He then began to take part in races in Europe. In 1900 he inaugurated the Coppa Florio race run on the mainland of Italy.

When Vincenzo Florio's enthusiasm spurred him to inaugurate a motor race around his beloved Sicily, people thought him mad. Sicily had no proper roads! Eventually a 92.48-mile circuit was worked out. The course began at the seafront near Cerda railway station then climbed into the mountains using tracks more suited to goats than cars, reaching a height of 3670 ft above sea level before beginning plunging down again. Another feature was a three-mile straight along the sea-front after Campofelice. The race was to be known as the Targa Florio (the Florio plate, or shield) and the circuit, embracing 2200 corners, was known as the *Grande Circuito delle Madonie* after the range of mountains it traversed.

The first race was run on May 6, 1906, although only 10 of the 22 entries made the start. A French shipping strike held up the Darracq and Mors teams. Winner was Alexandre Cagno at the wheel of an Itala; he took 9 h 32 m 22 s to cover three laps of the tortuous circuit, an average speed of 29.07 mph. There were six finishers, among them three other Italas in second, fourth and fifth positions. Cagno, from Turin, won a solid gold plate for his efforts. No fewer than 47 started the second Targa Florio in 1907 when Florio's great friend and former chauffeur Felice Nazzaro won in a FIAT at an average speed of 33.40 mph. His team-mate Vincenzo Lancia was second 12 minutes behind.

Only 13 cars started in 1908, despite the rapidly growing recognition of the race, now reduced to two laps. An Isotta Fraschini driven by Vincenzo Trucco won. The following year the Messina earthquake disrupted the race but Florio reduced the length of the race further to one lap and entered himself in a FIAT and several friends in De Dion Boutons, machines never intended for racing. Baron Francesco Ciuppa in a SPA beat Florio by a minute. The entries were poor once more in 1910—when F. Cariolato's Franco won the two-lap race at 29.10 mph but took an hour longer to complete the course that the winner of the combined *voiturette* event—and in 1911—when Ernesto Ceirano's SCAT also averaged 29.10 mph, but over three laps. The format was changed for 1912. Avoiding the mountains altogether, the race was incorporated with the *Giro di Sicilia*, a single lap of 652 miles to and from Palermo.

Florio drove a Mercedes in the 1912 event but became so over-tired that he drove himself up onto raised tram lines—and out of the race. A Florio *car* was also in the running, Vincenzo Florio having financed the short-lived project of an ambitious engineer from Turin. British driver Cyril Snipe, who worked in Turin, had over two hours' advantage at the wheel of his SCAT when he was overcome with exhaustion. He stopped his car, got out, laid down and fell asleep. His co-driver Pardini failed to arouse him for two hours. A bucket of water tossed over the slumbering Snipe had the desired effect as Snipe restarted and won by half an hour at an average speed of 24.30 mph.

The *Giro di Sicilia* format was retained until 1914, except that there was a half-way halt at Agrigenta. In

1913 Felice Nazzaro, formerly a driver for FIAT, appeared with a car of his own construction and won at 31.04 mph, while the following year Ernesto Ceirano's SCAT upped this to 38.94 mph.

Following World War I the race was revived at the end of November 1919. A decision was made to return to the mountains over a shorter course, the Medium Madonie which became known as the Polizzi circuit. Of 67.11 miles in length, it was a daunting prospect. The weather was fine at the startline, but 3000 ft up in the mountains there was snow, slush, mud and low clouds. The first to set off in the traditional staggered start pattern, was Enzo Ferrari, driving a CMN, but he was not to feature. The battle was between two Frenchmen, veteran René Thomas (Ballot) and the young, reckless André Boillot (Peugeot). Thomas crashed on one of the 1500 corners of the new Polizzi circuit, leaving Boillot the winner. But only just! Boillot, exhausted, skidded on the greasy track mere yards from the finish line. The Peugeot charged a wooden grandstand, but willing helpers put Boillot and his riding mechanic back in their seats and they engaged reverse gear to cross the line backwards. Ernest Ballot (the constructor of their crashed rivals car) feared disqualification for such a manoeuvre, and persuaded the tired crew to drive away, turn around and cross the line again front first! They

did, Boillot collapsing immediately afterwards murmuring, 'C'est pour la France'. The 1920 race—won by Guido Meregalli in a Nazzaro, a car built by the 1907 winner—was dull and held in terrible weather.

From 1921 until the mid-1930s the Targa Florio garnered increasing prestige. Works teams from all over Europe were attracted: Alfa Romeo, Fiat, Mercedes, Itala, Delage, Peugeot, Bugatti, Sunbeam and Ballot. Ranged against the cream of the professional factory drivers were top amateurs. In 1921 Italian Count Giulio Masetti, driving a 4.4-litre Grand Prix Fiat built in 1914, beat a solitary factory-entered 7.3-litre Mercedes 28/95 driven by Max Sailer. In 1922 Mercedes entered a full works team of six cars, but they were soundly beaten by a privately-entered Mercedes, the 4½-litre 1914 Grand Prix model of Masetti, who became the first driver to win two successive Targa Florios.

Ugo Sivocci and Antonio Ascari registered an Alfa Romeo 1-2 victory in 1923, the first of nine wins for the Milanese marque in a period of 48 years. The 15th running of the Targa Florio in 1924 saw it combine with the Coppa Florio. Targa competitors had to run four laps, as usual, then run an extra lap for the Coppa Florio. Following a battle with the Alfa Romeos of Ascari and Masetti, German Christian Werner triumphed in his 2-litre Mercedes.

Top: Vincenzo Lancia poses in his Fiat prior to the 1907 Targa Florio

Above left: a 1919 CMN awaiting the start of the Targa Florio; the driver is none other than a very young Enzo Ferrari

Above right: Achille Varzi and the PS Alfa Romeo at the 1930 event

Previous page: a Ferrari 512 competing in the 1970 Targa

From 1925 until 1929 Bugatti ruled the roost in Sicily. Meo Costantini, a Milanese who worked for Bugatti in Molsheim, conquered the works Peugeots in his 2-litre Bugatti T35. That year the Targa Florio was over five laps and the Coppa Florio over four, the same format being employed in 1926 when Costantini won again, this time with a 2.3-litre Bugatti T35T. It was a sad year, previous twice-winner Masetti being killed when his works Delage inexplicably overturned. Emilio Materassi, a new recruit to the·Bugatti team, won in 1927 in a 2-litre supercharged T35C, heading Count Conelli's 1½-litre supercharged T37A model. Elizabeth Junek, from Prague, entered her 2.3-litre Bugatti T35B, but retired early owing to steering problems, after holding fourth place behind three works-entered Bugattis at the end of the opening lap. Before the race Elizabeth and her husband Čenek had spent a month learning the circuit, including a lap on foot at the rate of 12 miles per day.

Elizabeth Junek was the sensation of the following year's race. She fought for the lead with such heroes as Albert Divo, the ultimate winner in a Bugatti T35B,

Above: Umberto Maglioli's 3-litre D23 Lancia seen during the 37th Targa Florio held in 1953; Maglioli went on to win the event at an average speed of 51.10 mph

Giuseppe Campari and Tazio Nuvolari, but a water leak caused the engine to overheat on the fifth and last lap and she dropped to fifth. (Sadly her husband was killed two months later and she retired from racing.) Fourth man Louis Chiron (Bugatti T35B) actually completed a sixth lap, claiming not to have realised the race was over! It was Dino once more in 1929 when only six of the 19 starters were able to take the record-breaking pace to finish.

The 1930 race was an epic struggle between Alfa Romeo and Bugatti. At the end there were two men straining every muscle, every nerve to seek the utmost from their over-worked machines: Achille Varzi and Louis Chiron. Varzi pinned his faith on a Grand Prix type 2-litre Alfa Romeo P2, a very difficult car to handle on this circuit, while Chiron hoped to score Bugatti's sixth win in his 2.3-litre Bugatti T35B. Both had problems. Chron crashed into a wall and had to change two wheels, while Varzi in trying to save time by refuelling from a can while still racing, set the rear of the car aflame. The verdict went to Varzi by a scant 1 m 48.4 s after almost seven hours of racing. Alfa Romeo won the next five races as well, thereby avenging Bugatti's glory.

Instead of an inter-marque battle the Targa Florio now became the personal feuding ground of arch-rivals

and ex-Alfa Romeo teammates, Achille Varzi and Tazio Nuvolari. Varzi borrowed a Bugatti T51 for the 22nd running of the race, which had to revert to the old Grand Madonie circuit (for four laps) after a cyclone destroyed roads and bridges on the Polizzi circuit. For three laps Varzi's red-painted Bugatti remained ahead, but then it rained and the Alfa Romeos, which were fitted with right-hand wings to protect their drivers from spray, had the advantage. Varzi, exhausted, finished first on the road but the Alfas had more than made up their difference of starting time and a jubilant Nuvolari was acclaimed the winner.

Vincenzo Florio successfully talked Mussolini into financing a loop road to avoid sections of the Polizzi circuit prone to bad weather conditions creating the *Piccolo Circuito delle Madonie*, at 44.74 miles, in 1932. It had to be covered eight times. Nuvolari triumphed once more in a 2.3-litre Alfa Romeo Monza from team-mate Baconin Borzacchini.

Marquis Antonio Brivio won the 1933 Targa Florio in a year in which Alfa Romeo seemed virtually unopposed, while in 1934 Varzi won in an Alfa Romeo when Nuvolari was absent. Brivio won again in 1935, leading seven Alfa Romeos in the first eight positions. Only two laps of the Piccolo Madonie circuit for 1½-litre sports cars comprised the December 1936 Targa Florio. Lancia took the first four places, headed by Magistri's 1.2-litre Augusta.

In 1937 Vincenzo Florio no longer held an official position in the Sicilian Automobile Club, which instituted completely different events: 1½-litre *voiturette* races at the *Parco della Favorita* on the outskirts of Palermo where a short and fast circuit was laid out. The race was run to this emaciated format for four years. Maseratis took the first three places each time. Francesco Severi's 6CM model triumphed in 1937, G. Rocco's similar model in 1938 and Luigi Villoresi won comfortably in both 1939 and 1940 with the new Maserati 4CL.

The Second World War left its mark on Sicily. The buildings along the sea-front at Palermo had been bombed into ruins, the grandstand at Cerda had been blown-up and the race control tower disassembled. The roads themselves were in an extremely poor state and when the Targa Florio returned to the motor racing calendar in 1948—with Vincenzo Florio also back in action—it was incorporated in the *Giro di Sicilia* series. Driving a 2-litre Ferrari 166 Mille Miglia, veteran Clemente Biondetti and his co-driver Count Igor Troubetskoy easily won the race with the 1100 cc Fiat-engined works Cisitalias of Taruffi/Rabbia and Machieraldo/Savio an encouraging second and third. Rain, thunderstorms and fog marred the running of the 1949 race when a British car led until shortly after distance. This was the Bristol-engined Frazer-Nash High Speed model shared by Dorino Serafini/Rudi Haller, but it was to skid in the treacherous conditions and bend a steering arm. The race was now contested between last year's winner Biondetti in the Ferrari and Franco Rol in a 2½-litre Alfa Romeo. With Rol delayed over five minutes at a level crossing, Biondetti won by 2 m 51 s in a race lasting 13 h 15 m 9 s.

The last Targa Florio of the *Giro di Sicilia* format was in 1950, proving a real race of attrition with 79 finishers from 186 starters. One leader after another succumbed to mechanical failure, leaving Mario and Franco Bornigia to win in a 2½-litre Alfa Romeo.

In 1951 it was back to the Piccolo Madonie circuit. From 25 starters there were only eight finishers. Giovanni Bracco's 4.1-litre Ferrari 340 America set a sizzling pace, but its suspension wilted under the strain and Franco Cortese came through to win after a cool, calculated drive in a 2-litre Frazer-Nash Le Mans Replica. It was the first—and only—victory by a British car. Bracco, taking over a 2.5-litre Ferrari 212 Sport, salvaged second place and also broke the lap record, recording 52 m 24.8 s on his sixth lap. Lancias swept the board with a 1-2-3 victory in 1952, but only after Bracco's big Ferrari had retired early, Giulio Cabianca's tiny 1350 cc OSCA had broken its back axle on the seventh of the eight laps and Cartese's well-

known 'Nash had fallen into a ditch on the very last lap. Winner Felice Bonetto almost did not make it. His 2-litre Lancia Aurelia GT ran out of petrol on the long Buonfornello straight leading to the start/finish area. He borrowed a litre of fuel but this, too, was consumed mere yards from the line. Bonetto pushed his car uphill and, on the point of collapse, climbed aboard to cross the line on the starter motor. Bonetto still set a new winning average of 49.73 mph while Cabianca's little OSCA had lowered the circuit record to 51 m 17.4 s, 52.34 mph.

Lancia returned in 1953 with a team of 3-litre sports-racing models, the D23s. Umberto Maglioli won at 51.10 mph and team-mate Piero Taruffi became the first lap record holder at under 50 m, recording 49 m 37.0 s, 54.10 mph. In 1954 Lancia won again, Taruffi in a 3.3-litre D24 averaging a record 55.88 mph to beat Luigi Musso's 2-litre Maserati A6GCS by over 7½ minutes. Musso, the initial leader, had lost several minutes owing to sickness, having eaten unwisely the night before. Taruffi's team-mate Eugenio Castellotti crashed his Lancia D24 not before he also smashed the lap record with 57.86 mph.

The Targa Florio received a great accolade in 1955 when it became a qualifying round of the World Sports Car Championship. The race distance was lengthened to 13 laps and, with an October date, it became the final and deciding round of the series. Prior to the race Ferrari led with 19 points, three more than either Mercedes-Benz and Jaguar. When Jaguar decided not to enter, it became a two-way battle. Stirling Moss's 3-litre Mercedes-Benz 300SLR set the early pace, but on lap 4 the Englishman overshot a bend and landed six foot down in a field. The car was lightly damaged and with the aid of a large band of peasants it was

manhandled back on to the track. Repaired as best as possible in the pits, the Mercedes was taken over by Peter Collins who proved as fast as his partner and the pair moved into the lead again. Team-mates Juan Manuel Fangio/Karl Kling were second, to ensure Mercedes won the championship, with the best Ferrari placing third. This was the 3.4-litre 860 Monza model crewed by Eugenio Castellotti/Robert Manzon. Moss lowered the lap record to 43 m 7.4 s, 62.22 mph.

The race was not in the 1956 World Sports Car Championship series, providing a surprise win for Porsche. The tiny, 1500 cc Porsche RS was driven by Umberto Maglioli, an experienced driver thoroughly at

home in the Sicilian mountains, and German Huschke von Hanstein. Giulio Cabianca (1.5-litre OSCA) was initially awarded second place, but as his co-driver Luigi Villoresi had already driven another entry he was disqualified and the place given to Piero Taruffi (3-litre Maserati 300S). In 1957, the year of the Mille Miglia disaster in which two drivers and 11 spectators were killed, the Targa Florio was run as a regularity trial.

The race was back with a vengeance in 1958, over 14 laps and back in the championship calendar. Stirling Moss set the pace in his works Aston Martin DBR 1/300, breaking the lap record with 42 m 17.5 s, 63.47 mph, but its gearbox broke, leaving Luigi Musso/Olivier Gendebien to win in a Ferrari 250 Testa Rossa. Ferrari's attack in the 1959 event failed, leaving the race a Porsche procession. Germans Edgar Barth/Wolfgang Seidel won in a 1½-litre works-entered Porsche RSK, finishing 20 m in front of the privately-entered Porsche RS of Eberhard Mahle/Paul Strahle/Herbert Linge.

After Vincenzo Florio died at 76, there might not have been a Targa Florio in 1959, or any subsequent year. Fortunately his widow Lucia Florio, aided by her

Below: the winner of the 1967 Targa, the Porsche 910/8 of Paul Hawkins and Rolf Stommelen blasts through Collesano on its way to victory

Above left: the Phil Hill/Hap Sharp Chaparral 2F coupé in action during the 1967 event

Opposite page, clockwise: an Alfa Romeo pictured during the 1968 event;

the Parkes/Müller Ferrari near Campofelice in 1970;

Rolf Stommelen and the works Alfa Romeo in action in the 1973 Targa

grandson Paladino and other Sicilians, ensured the race would carry on. In the 1960s the Targa Florio became unique as a road race. When great strides were made in motor racing safety, few people thought it could survive into the 1970s. Although it remained part of the sports car championship scene, it did not always attract full factory participation. However, it continued to be supported by a host of amateur drivers in varying types of machinery, people who loved this relic of the past in the modern era of hygenic 'safe' tracks.

Umberto Maglioli put up a brave show with a 2.9-litre Maserati T61, but a ruptured fuel tank caused its retirement and the 10-lap 1960 Targa Florio belonged to Jo Bonnier/Hans Herrmann in a 1.7-litre Porsche RS60. Six minutes behind followed the 2.4-litre Ferrari Dino 246s of Phil Hill/Wolfgang von Trips. In 1961 Stirling Moss/Graham Hill appeared all set for victory in a 2-litre Porsche RS61, but six miles from the finish, when holding a comfortable lead, Moss had the transmission seize owing to lack of oil. This gave victory to the works Ferrari Dino 246s of Wolfgang von Trips/Olivier Gendebien; on his last lap von Trips cracked the lap record with 40 m 3.4 s, 67.01 mph. It was Ferrari *v* Porsche once more in 1962 when the Italian team won again. A 2.4-litre Dino 246SP driven by the trio Ricardo Rodriguez/Willy Mairesse/Olivier Gendebien led home their team-mates Giancarlo Baghetti/Lorenzo Bandini (2-litre Ferrari Dino 196SP) by $11\frac{1}{2}$ minutes. Mairesse lowered the record to 40 m 0.3 s, 67.06 mph. However, the 1963 race was a disaster for Ferrari. His own car having broken-down, fiery Belgian Willy Mairesse took over the 2-litre Ferrari Dino 196SP driven by Lorenzo Bandini/Lodovico Scarfiotti and, with victory in sight, he spun on the final lap. Dragging his rear engine cover, the car made it to the finish line 12 s behind the eight-cylinder Porsche 718 coupé raced by Jo Bonnier and Carlo Mario Abate.

Ferrari did not enter the 1964 race, while the Porsche prototypes retired, leaving victory to Colin Davis/Antonio Pucci in a GT Porsche 904 GTs. A team of Anglo-American AC Cobras was entered, but although team leader Dan Gurney worked his way up to second place the big, 4.7-litre machines were not suited to the rough circuit and fell back with suspension

damage. Ferrari returned in 1965 when Sicilian school-teacher Nino Vaccarella set a scorching pace in the 3.3-litre Ferrari 275P2 he shared with Lorenzo Bandini. The pair won by over 4 m and Vaccarella set the first sub-40 m lap record: 39 m 21.0 s, 68.21 mph. With the failure of the two other Ferrari prototypes and an open Ford GT40, works Porsches occupied second, third and fourth positions.

In 1966 the pace was so quick in treacherously wet conditions that the favourites—works-entered Ferraris and Porsches—failed, allowing the Swiss-entered Porsche 906 crewed by Willy Mairesse/Herbert Müller to win the 50th Targa Florio very easily. That remarkable machine, the 7-litre Chevrolet-engined Chaparral 2F, ran in the 1967 race. The winged car, crewed by Americans Phil Hill/Hap Sharp, was not suited to the roads but was in fourth place when its transmission failed on lap 9. Ferrari's singleton entry of a 4-litre 330P4 for Nino Vaccarella/Lodovico Scarfiotti was out on the very first lap when Vaccarella hit a wall, and ultimately the race developed into another Porsche benefit, the German cars taking the first three places led by the 2.2-litre 910/8 of Paul Hawkins/Rolf Stommelen. Swiss Herbert Müller, at the wheel of a 4-litre Ferrari 365P3/4, set best lap of 37 m 9.0 s, 72.25 mph. Alfa Romeo almost took the laurels the following year as the Nanni Galli/Ignazio Giunti 2-litre T33 led into the last lap. But Vic Elford, rally-turned-racing star, was in rare form. His 2.2-litre Porsche 907 had lost 17 m on the first lap when a wheel came off—twice!—and his co-driver, the veteran Umberto Maglioli, was not as fast as before, but by lowering the record to an amazing 36 m 2.3 s, 74.49 mph, Elford snatched victory by almost 3 m. In 1969 Elford reduced his record still further to 35 m 8.2 s, 76.39 mph, but a broken alternator belt dropped him to second behind the sister works Porsche 908/02 Spyder of Gerhard Mitter/Udo Schütz.

Porsche, knowing their 5-litre 917s to be unsuited to the Piccolo Madonie circuit, built new cars especially for the 1970 Targa Florio, the short-wheelbase 908/03 Spyders. They were first, second and fifth (Jo Siffert/Brian Redman, Pedro Rodriguez/Leo Kinnunen, Dickie Attwood/Björn Waldegård) in the 11-lap race, and Kinnunen established a resounding lap record of 33 m 36.0 s, 79.89 mph, a time never to be beaten. Nino Vaccarella/Ignazio Giunti bravely drove a big 5-litre Ferrari 512S and were rewarded with a fine third place.

Porsche's run of five successive victories was halted in 1971. With the German cars running into un-characteristic trouble early in the race, the works Alfa Romeo T33/3s took first and second places. Nino Vaccarella shared the winning car with Toine Hezemans, while Andrea de Adamich/Gijs van Lennep followed them home 1 m 11.7 s behind. Alfa were favourites once more in 1972 for only a lone works Ferrari 312P crewed by Arturo Merzario/Sandro Munari opposed their four entries. Vic Elford's Alfa Romeo T33TT/3 blew-up on the first lap, then the engine failed on the Nino Vaccarella/Rolf Stommelen car. Later Toine Hezemans, sharing his Alfa with Andrea de Adamich, broke a wheel and lost valuable time, but still the Nanni Galli/Helmut Marko car led the Ferrari. Drama intervened when Galli spun avoiding a backmarker and lost two minutes restarting; although co-driver Marko made up ground quickly, the Ferrari triumphed by 16.9 s.

Before the 1973 race the FIA announced that the Targa Florio would lose its championship status the following year. The race was now unsuited to the sports-prototypes of the 1970s, but Alfa Romeo and

Ferrari entered two cars each. All four failed, however, leaving victory to a Martini-sponsored works Porsche 911 Carrera RSR crewed by Gijs van Lennep/Herbert Müller and a car equally suited to the tough Sicilian track, Sandro Munari and Jean-Claude Andruet's 2.4-litre Lancia Stratos.

A non-championship GT Targa Florio, run over seven laps, was held in 1974. It was won by the Lancia Stratos of Gérard Larrousse/Amilcar Ballestrieri. No race was inscribed on the 1975 international calendar. Sports cars *did* go to Sicily for a championship race, however, but it was not to the projected 3.75-mile artificial road circuit at Cerda talked about in the past by the Automobile Club di Palermo where they had hoped to run future Targa Florios. They went to Enna, a Sicilian track completely unconnected with the Targa Florio.

MK

Top: the Van Lennep/Müller Porsche, winner of the 1973 event

Centre: frantic activity in the pits

Bottom: Nino Vaccarella in action in an Alfa Romeo 33 in 1971. Vaccarella, being a Sicilian, was the favourite with the crowds whenever he took part in the Targa Florio

The Silver Fox

AN ENGINEER, a racing driver, a motor-cycle racer, a record-breaker and a team manager, Piero Taruffi enjoyed a long and involved career participating in motor-sport, stopping only when he had satisfied his greatest ambition: to win the Mille Miglia. This was in 1957, when he was fifty, 27 years after his first attempt at this classic Italian road race. He was known as the Silver Fox because of his grey hair.

Born on 12 October 1906, Taruffi was presented with a 350 cc AJS racing motor cycle and entered for his first race in January 1925. At the Monte Mario hill-climb near Rome the enthusiastic eighteen-year-old was second overall and winner of the 350 cc class. More successes followed with a variety of machines: P&M, Guzzi, Norton and OPRA. It was inevitable that Taruffi would move on to four wheels and he was invited to co-drive his friend Lelio Pellegrini's 2.3-litre Bugatti on the 1930 Mille Miglia. After problems with loose wiring, overheating and misfiring, they were fortieth.

Next they entered the Tunis–Tripoli regularity trial and won in Pellegrini's Alfa Romeo 1750. In 1931 Pellegrini acquired a 2-litre Itala Model 65 sports car and it was entered for several hill-climbs and races. At the Montenaro circuit he was eighth behind top-line drivers and following some minor race wins plus a 112 mph lap on his Norton

motor cycle at Monza Taruffi was invited to drive for Scuderia Ferrari.

Taruffi won his two events for Ferrari at the end of 1931, driving a 2.3-litre Alfa Romeo to victory in the Lake of Bolsena regularity trial and the Coppa Frigo hill-climb. In 1932 he led the Mille Miglia, but was side-lined with electrical and engine faults. He was second in Rome's Royal Grand Prix and the Francorchamps 24-hours and won the Coppa Grand Sasso race and the Coppa Frigo hill-climb. In 1933, Enzo Ferrari took over the responsibility of running the works Alfa Romeo team; he had more drivers than cars, which meant missing some races.

Piero thought of returning to motor cycles, but with the aid of two friends purchased a 3-litre Maserati 8C for 1934. He also joined an aeronautical and motor cycle firm, assisting on development. After a fifth place in the Mille Miglia in an 1100 cc Maserati, he was invited to drive Maserati's most fearsome car in the Tripoli Grand Prix. The V5 model, it featured a $4\frac{1}{2}$ litre V16 engine which developed 350 bhp. However, Taruffi locked his brakes at the end of a very fast straight and crashed heavily, putting himself in hospital for several weeks. He emerged to be offered a Scuderia Ferrari Alfa Romeo.

Following World War II, Taruffi was invited to join Piero Dusio's Cisitalia set-up in Turin; the single-seater Cisitalias were small, using 1100 cc Fiat engines. As well as overseeing these machines he raced them, winning his class in the 1947 Italian Championship. Driving an 1100 cc Cisitalia sports car he was second overall and class winner in the 1948 Giro di Sicilia. That year Piero

Below: Piero Taruffi and the twin-boom, Gilera-engined Tarf record breaker

also gained four world speed records in Tarf 1, a Guzzi motor-cycle-engined 'twin-boom' record-breaking car. With Guzzi, Gilera and Maserati-engined Tarfs Taruffi continued to break records until his retirement in 1957.

Taruffi raced for many teams in the immediate post-war years, but he rejoined the Ferrari team in 1951. The highlights of the year was victory in the Carrera Panamericana in a 2.6-litre Ferrari 212 Export shared with Luigi Chinetti. During the following year, in which he married Isabella, he won his only World Championship Grand Prix, the Swiss at Berne, in a 2-litre Ferrari 500. He was ultimately third in the championship. He also raced in Britain, driving Tony Vandervell's Thin Wall Special (a modified $4\frac{1}{2}$-litre Ferrari 375) to victory at Dundrod and Silverstone, while he sampled a 500 cc Cooper at Brands Hatch.

In 1953, Piero was invited to join the Lancia sports-car team, but the car broke down in the Mille Miglia, the Targa Florio (when he crashed while leading, having mistaken a pit signal) and Le Mans. In the following year, the Mille Miglia slipped out of his grasp yet again when a slower car moved over and caused Taruffi to crash his leading Lancia. He did, however, win the Targa Florio and the Giro di Sicilia. Lancia withdrew from sports-car races at the end of 1954, so Taruffi went back to Ferrari for next season. He won the Giro di Sicilia in a 3.7-litre Ferrari 118LM, but quit the team at the end of the year after a row with Enzo Ferrari about a suitable car for the Targa Florio.

The 1956 season was disappointing. He raced for Maserati in sports-car events and accepted the offer of a British Vanwall for the Italian Grands Prix, being sidelined with transmission failure. In 1957, fifty-year-old Taruffi was still racing. He was a member of the works Chevrolet team in the Sebring twelve-hours and drove a Formula One Maserati 250F to fourth place in the Syracuse Grand Prix. For the Mille Miglia he was offered a works Ferrari, a 4-litre 335 Sport. Despite almost giving up when rain made conditions frightening, Taruffi crossed the finish line to be told by Isabella he had won. He did not know rival Peter Collins had retired within 125 miles of the finish! Taruffi had won the Mille Miglia at last! MK

ON TOP DOWN UNDER

The Tasman Series was once the winter pleasure of Europe's top drivers, but a longer GP season has changed all that

AUSTRALIA AND NEW ZEALAND are well-established in the world of motor racing despite their relatively small populations. The Australian Grand Prix was inaugurated in 1928 and New Zealand's in 1954. Since the 1950s Europeans—both top names and amateurs—have been attracted to early-season races in New Zealand and Australia, and ultimately the inevitable happened. The Confederation of Australian Motor Sport and the Association of New Zealand Car Clubs met and arranged a championship, the Tasman Cup series, which was inaugurated in 1964.

Until 1969 the Tasman Formula was exclusively for single-seater racing cars of up to 2500 cc, a figure which bore no relation to any FIA formula. Initially it really meant that home-based drivers could use the old, four-cylinder Coventry Climax FPF engine—a relic from the $2\frac{1}{2}$-litre Formula 1 of 1954–60—while overseas visitors were also obliged to employ this well-tried unit. Later the Europeans gained a great advantage as they used either 'stretched' multi-cylinder engines from the $1\frac{1}{2}$-litre Formula One of 1961–65 or lowered the capacity of modern engines from the 3-litre Formula

with short strokes. The 1.75-mile Levin circuit at Palmerston North saw Hulme romp away from Mayer and McLaren, but McLaren turned the tables in the 2.21-mile New Zealand Grand Prix at Pukekohe, winning from Hulme and Mayer. It was Bruce's first victory in his home Grand Prix. Brabham, making a late start to the series, collided with New Zealander Tony Shelly's Lotus 18/21-Climax. McLaren won again at the Lady Wigram Trophy Race and the Teretonga Trophy, but blew up in the first Australian round, the Grand Prix at Sandown Park. This went to Brabham from Bib Stillwell's Brabham BT4-Climax. Brabham won again at Warwick Farm (a 2.25-mile course laid out Aintree style, along a horse-racing track), but McLaren was only 0.4 s in arrears and held on to his championship lead. Local driver Frank Matich (Brabham BT7-Climax) had led for three laps before spinning, while Graham Hill joined in the series in David McKay's Brabham BT4-Climax and was fourth. At Lakeside Park, Brabham scored his third successive victory from Aussie John Youl's Cooper T53-Climax and McLaren, who had now scored sufficient points to clinch the series. The final round at Longford was clouded by the tragic death of young Timmy Mayer, the American's Cooper flying off the road after a sharp rise and crashing into a tree. Hill won after Brabham retired, beating McLaren and Matich. The final points score read: McLaren, 39; Brabham, 33; Hulme and Mayer, 23.

Reigning champion Bruce McLaren re-entered the fray in 1965 with a new Cooper T79 plus a '64 model T70 for American Phil Hill. Lotus ran a works car, a modified Formula Two 32B for Jim Clark. New Brabham BT11As were on hand for Jack Brabham (who ran in the Australian section only), Graham Hill (who also had an abbreviated series), plus locals Frank Gardner and Bib Stillwell, while older models were on hand for New Zealand star Jim Palmer, Frank Matich and Australian veteran Lex Davison. Kick-off was the New Zealand Grand Prix at Pukekohe where Hill led virtually the entire distance. Clark and McLaren collided, the former retiring on the spot. Clark then won at Levin, Wigram and Teretonga in quick succession, going to Australia with a three-point lead over Frank Gardner. Clark won once more at Warwick Farm (where Hill spun on the last lap and dropped to fifth behind Brabham, Matich and Stillwell), but lost out to Brabham at Sandown Park owing to fading oil pressure. Nevertheless second was sufficient to sew up the series with one round, the Australian Grand Prix at Longford, still to be run. McLaren won this, making up for a troublesome season owing to tyre problems and moving up to second position in the championship with 24 to Clark's 35 points. Brabham was third with 21. (Clark also won the fourth Australian race at Lakeside, a non-championship event.)

How long could the old Climax FPF engine last? Now well past its prime, it faced a strong challenge in the 1966 Tasman Cup series. With the new 3-litre Formula One pre-occupying them, McLaren declined to enter while Brabham decided to enter his Repco V8-engined Brabham BT19 for the final two Australian rounds only. Favourites were obviously the 1.9-litre V8 BRM P261s of Graham Hill and Jackie Stewart (Hill was only contracted to participate in one New Zealand round, his deputy being Dickie Attwood.) The rot began for the old Climax '4s' in the New Zealand Grand Prix with Hill and Stewart scoring an easy 1–2. Lotus, who retained Climax FPF power for the Lotus 39 driven by defending champion Jim Clark, went out with gearbox failure. Frank Gardner's Climax-engined Brabham BT11A seemed to have Levin in the bag, with two laps to go the drive-shaft failed and Attwood

Above left: Bruce McLaren, a New Zealander, first holder of the Tasman Cup in 1964, holds his trophy aloft after the final round at Longford. It was an event with bitter-sweet memories for McLaren; he won the championship, but his friend and team-mate Timmy Meyer was killed in practice

Above: start of the New Zealand Grand Prix of 1969

Left: Graham McRae and his McRae GM2 in action during the 1974 Tasman Cup series. McRae is a three-times Tasman Cup winner

One which was introduced in 1966. From 1970 Formula 5000 cars were allowed to participate and although the 5-litre 'stock-block' engines were superior to the 2½-litre pure racing units, it was not until the following year that a Formula 5000 car won the championship.

Since its inauguration the Tasman Cup series has been won six times by a New Zealander (Bruce McLaren, 1964; Chris Amon, 1969; Graeme Lawrence, 1970; Graham McRae, 1971–72–73), five times by a British driver (Jim Clark, 1965–67–68; Jackie Stewart, 1966; Peter Gethin, 1974) and only once by an Australian (Warwick Brown, 1975).

The Tasman Cup series was officially inaugurated for 1964. The New Zealand and Australian organisers felt it added more prestige to their races and was an added incentive for overseas entries to compete in every round. (It is interesting to calculate that in 1962 and 1963, had there been a championship, the winners would have been Stirling Moss and Bruce McLaren respectively.) Instead of catering for *formula libre* machinery, however, an official Tasman Formula was drawn up. This set an engine capacity limit of 2½-litres and cars had to run on petrol; beforehand some Coventry Climax FPF engines, the almost universal unit 'Down Under', had been of 2750 cc capacity and ran on alcohol-based fuel.

The entry for 1964 was as good as ever. Brabham ran two works cars, Hulme's '63-model BT4-Climax and Jack's new BT7. Bruce McLaren commissioned Cooper to build two lightweight cars, the T70s, for himself and American Tim Mayer to pilot. Chris Amon arrived with an ex-Bowmaker Lola Mk 4. All the top cars used 2.5-litre Climax engines, some ex-2.7 units

inherited the lead. Clark was second. BRMs triumphed once more at Wigram with a Stewart-Attwood 1–2 and it was Stewart once more at Teretonga. Clark won the first Australian round at Warwick Farm with Hill second, while Hill won at Lakeside and Stewart at Sandown Park to clinch the championship. To underline their superiority Stewart and Hill made it a BRM 1–2 *finale* at Longford.

It was almost the same story in 1967. BRMs entered Stewart to defend his title in the same BRM P261, but now with an uprated 2.1-litre V8 engine, with Dickie Attwood and new recruits Piers Courage and Chris Irwin to back him up in the second entry. Clark considered his Lotus 33 with its more modern 2-litre Climax FWMV engine a more likely weapon for the series, while Brabham entered two cars with full 2½-litre Repco V8 engines. 'Black Jack' himself handled a Formula Two-based BT23A, while Denny Hulme sampled an older-specification BT22. Stewart won at Pukekohe on the revised 1.75-mile circuit, and although

Clark won at Levin it was in vain so far as the championship was concerned as both Levin and Teretonga did not qualify for points. Clark won at Wigram and Teretonga, while into the Australian section Clark won at Lakeside, was second to Stewart at Warwick Farm and won at Sandown Park to take the series for the second time. At Longford, however, Brabham came through to beat Clark. Final scores were: Clark, 45; Stewart, Gardner and Brabham, 18 (Gardner drove the only competitive Climax FPF-engined car, a lightweight Formula Two-based Brabham BT18).

Top: Jackie Stewart (BRM) and Jim Clark (Lotus) fight for supremacy in 1966

Above: the 4½-mile Longford track in Tasmania comprised genuine roads complete with level crossings and wooden bridges

The final blow for the old Climax, if one was needed, came in 1968 when 2½-litre versions of the new Ford DFV Formula One engine (known as the DFW) employed in up-to-date chassis—two works Gold Leaf Lotus 49Ts for Jim Clark and Graham Hill—made an appearance. Local drivers no longer had a chance, although European-based New Zealander Chris Amon arranged to drive a Formula Two-type Ferrari with a 2.4-litre Dino V6 engine. BRM brought along two brand new V12-engined P126s (plus an old 2.1-litre P261 V8 as a spare). Alfa Romeo was another source of power, an Italian V8 finding its way into Alec Mildren's Brabham BT23D driven by Frank Gardner. The contest developed into a Clark v Amon struggle. Amon won at Pukekohe and Levin, but Clark turned the tables at Wigram. Bruce McLaren, 'guest' BRM driver in New Zealand, won in the wet at Teretonga after Clark had an accident, while it was nearly all Clark in Australia as he won at Surfers Paradise (a 2-mile circuit near Brisbane), Warwick Farm and Sandown Park. Young Englishman Piers Courage turned the tables at

Longford when he took his 1600 cc Formula Two McLaren M4A to victory in the wet. Clark narrowly won the championship, with 44 points to Amon's 36. Courage, by dint of several brilliant drives, was third with 34.

Two Ferrari Dino 246s for Chris Amon and Derek Bell; two Lotus 49T-Fords for Jochen Rindt and Graham Hill; a Frank Williams-entered Brabham BT24-Ford for Piers Courage; plus a British-designed, Australian-financed Mildren-Alfa Romeo for Frank Gardner spearheaded the last of the 'classic' Tasman Cups in 1969. Jack Brabham, who raced in only two 1968 rounds in his BT23E-Repco, was destined to run in but one event this year in the Formula Three-based Brabham BT31 with Repco T830 engine. It was Amon's series with wins at Pukekohe, Levin, Lakeside and Sandown Park, with Rindt second despite many problems—including a serious accident—in his Lotus. Rindt beat team-mate Hill at Wigram and also won at Warwick Farm. Courage won at Teretonga.

In an effort to reduce costs and put their local drivers on par with the visitors, the Tasman Cup organisers opened the 1970 series to Formula 5000 cars as well as single-seaters with 2½-litre pure racing engines. Four Europeans plus five American drivers of differing ability, led by Derek Bell's Wheatcroft Racing Brabham BT26A-Ford, comprised the overseas contingent. And they didn't win a race! To confuse matters further, although the 5-litre 'stock-block' F5000 McLaren M10A-Chevrolets won five of the seven races, New Zealander Graeme Lawrence in his ex-Amon 2½-litre Ferrari Dino 246, with one race win to his credit, took the championship through sheer reliability.

The Tasman Cup series was indeed different. The emphasis became more on Formula 5000 and local drivers and, with less money on offer, the visitors who did come from Europe, America (or even Japan on one occasion) often found themselves in difficulties so far from home. With a race each weekend plus thousands of miles of travelling there was no time to spare.

In 1971 Graham McRae, a boastful New Zealander who is a brilliant engineer as well as a racing driver, won the championship in his McLaren M10B-Chevrolet and repeated the dose early in 1972 in a car largely of his own design named the Leda LT27-Chevrolet. The same car, renamed the McRae GM1-Chevrolet following Leda's take-over, gave McRae the first ever Tasman Cup hat-trick in 1973. The following year McRae's new GM2-Chevrolet was definitely the fastest car in the series, but not the most reliable. The Tasman title fell to the last European entrant in the series, British driver Peter Gethin at the wheel of a works-supported Chevron B24-Chevrolet entered by the Belgian Racing Team VDS. In 1975 but for Chris Amon's American-entered Talon MR1-Chevrolet it was a local affair and for the first time an Australian driver clinched the series, young Warwick Brown with his Lola T332-Chevrolet taking the honours by one point after a bitterly fought contest.

The change in Tasman Cup format certainly meant closer, more exciting racing. It also meant that so far as the rest of the world was concerned the championship counted for little with no top names competing. Its future seems shaky. Rothmans, under the Peter Stuyvesant banner, sponsored the series in 1974 and 1975, but the politics between New Zealand and Australian organisers was such that the cigarette company announced they were to abandon their support for 1976. It is possible that the series will revert to what it was in the pre-Tasman Cup days, as selection of motor races in New Zealand and Australia in the opening months of the year. But without top names. . . .   MK

BUILT BEHIND THE IRON CURTAIN

As first Nesseldorf and later Tatra, this Czech establishment could boast that it employed one of the world's great designers: Hans Ledwinka

Below: the original Tatras were known as Nesseldorfs; this is the two-seater Nesseldorf President model of 1899; it was powered by a twin-cylinder Benz engine

THE FOUNDATIONS OF THE Czech firm of Tatra were laid in the Northern Moravian village of Nesselsdorf 125 years ago by a pair of enterprising carpenters and wheelwrights, Ignac Sustala and Adolf Raska who established the original coach and cart manufacturing business in 1859. Three years later they were able to build a small factory, and by 1856 sales had become sufficiently brisk for the establishment of a branch in Lwow. Another branch followed in Ratibor, Prussia, in 1864, and retail premises in Wroclaw, Vienna, Prague, and Berlin. The firm became known in the 1860s for its Neutischeinek buggies, and the production of open and closed luxury coaches.

Through the 1870s the firm earned awards in several important industrial exhibitions. Construction of the Nesselsdorf factory was completed, and by 1880 it employed 150 workers and produced 1200 vehicles a year. The construction of the Studenky-Stramberk railway line in 1882 opened a new chapter for the firm. The call for railway carriages provoked considerable

Three types were available with 8 hp, 12 hp and four-cylinder 24 hp engines, but were not particularly successful. Ledwinka, who had quit Nesselsdorf for a brief period to work on steam cars with Friedmann in Vienna, was brought back to reorganise the Nesselsdorf car division and to design new models.

In 1906 his successful S Type was produced and established the firm's reputation world-wide as a car maker. It had a 3.3-litre four-cylinder engine with the cylinders cast in pairs and a vertically driven overhead camshaft arrangement, known as the Glockengetriebe. Rear axle drive was through a Cardan shaft and a transmission with two gear rings in the case and three gear wheels to provide four forward speeds and a reverse. The succeeding T type used a monobloc engine, as did the six-cylinder U40/50PS and U40/65PS cars which followed. All had a proper chassis and cartspring suspension with engine and transmission located in what was to become the conventional position, as opposed to the tip-off body, axle-mounted engine and twin rear chain drive of the earlier cars.

The T and U types were produced around the beginning of World War I, the top 65 hp six-cylinder

extension of the factory, including a bigger forging shop and a new assembly area with a carpentry and cabinet-makers' section. In 1891 the enterprise was turned into a joint stock company, with a working capital of two million Austrian crowns.

The firm moved into motor manufacture in 1897 through the combined enthusiasms of factory general manager, Hugo Fischer, and a local motoring pioneer, Baron von Liebig. A new company, Nesselsdorf, was established with offices in Vienna, and the Austro-Hungarian Empire's first motor car, the President, was designed around a 5 hp Benz flat-twin engine. It covered the 320 kilometers from Nesselsdorf to Vienna in May 1898 to appear at an exhibition there, the journey taking 14½ hours. One of the engineers involved in the President design was Edmund Rumpler, who was later associated with Adler and who, after the First World War, was to build cars under his own name. In the same year the factory began work on the prototype of a two-ton truck, powered by a flat-four engine with a three-speed gearbox and a maximum speed of 20 kph.

Also involved in the design of Central Europe's first car was Hans Ledwinka, soon to become one of the great names in early car development. The President, of which ten were built with chain drive to the counter-shaft and pneumatic tyres, was followed in 1899 by the Meteor with a twin-cylinder 6 hp engine, and then by the Spitzbub model.

The turn of the century saw a new Nesselsdorf car similar to the previous models, but in that same year the decision was taken to build the firm's own engine.

Because the factory did not have the capacity to produce engines, this task was given to the Viennese firm of William Hardy, and Nesselsdorf engines were produced from 1900. In the same year, a pure racing car was designed by Ledwinka with Von Liebig's continued support around a twin-cylinder 12 hp Benz engine and four-speed gearbox. With a top speed of 112 kph the car was successful, von Liebig winning the Nice–La Turbie race of 1900, and taking second place in the Salzburg–Linz–Vienna event. The car also contested the Paris–Vienna and Gordon Bennett races. A prototype bus and an experimental electric car were also built.

The Nesselsdorf car of 1900 was similar in design to earlier cars, but a year later the engine was placed under the chassis and the old carriage-style body was dropped.

Above: the Tatra 17/31 produced between 1926 and 1931

Right: the unusual Tatra V370 prototype of 1933 was powered by a twin-cylinder engine

Below: the luxurious Tatra 11 saloon of 1923

Right: 1934 Tatra 54 two-door convertible; it was fitted with a 1484 cc, 12 hp, air-cooled engine

Below: front and rear-end views of the interesting Ledwinka-designed Tatra 77

car having the innovation of four-wheel braking. The Nesselsdorf car division produced many T type cars for military use during this period, though an exclusive model with 20/30 hp engine was built for the Emperor of Austria in 1915. The division also manufactured TL2 two-ton trucks of 35 hp utilising S and T type car transmissions with very little modification.

Production was not huge—in 1915 only 105 trucks were produced—but it was growing quickly, with 226 in 1916 and 342 in 1917, by which time the factory employed 2,500 people. A TL4 four-ton truck was introduced during this period.

The end of World War I found Nesselsdorf within the boundaries of the new independent state of Czechoslovakia, and renamed Koprivnice, and in 1920 the old Nesselsdorfer Wagenbau firm became Koprivnice Vozovka A.S. Test runs to prove a new design of braking for Nesselsdorf lorries had been taking place in the High Tatra mountains, and the Tatra name was adopted. By 1920 the last NW badge (for Nesselsdorfer Wagenbau) had given way to the Tatra trade mark.

Ledwinka, who had worked for Steyr during the war, returned to his old firm and set about designing an 'everyman's car for Tatra, foreseeing the increasingly limited market for the large, complex and luxurious car of the pre-war days. His new model, the Tatra 11, was designed for long life, ease of maintenance, and low fuel consumption, and this car turned out to be one of the classics of automobile design.

Presented in public for the first time at the Prague Motor Show of 1923, the Tatra 11 had an air-cooled 1056 cc two-cylinder engine producing 12 hp, rigidly connected to the clutch housing and thence the trans-

mission housing. The car had a backbone tubular frame and featured rear swing axles, differential, and independent suspension all round. This concept put Tatra ahead of most car firms of the day in terms of design, and was the basis of subsequent Tatra cars and commercial vehicles.

The Tatra 11 was not designed as a competition car, but the soundness of the basic design made it eminently suitable for racing and hill-climbing compared with most of the older designs still in use. In 1924 works driver Vermirovsky swept the board with this model at the Solitude hillclimb, near Stuttgart. The following year the car took first and second class places in the Targa Florio, driven by Fritz Hückel and Karl Sponer. These were standard production cars with the exception of swinging half axles in place of leaf springs at the front, and twin inlet valves instead of single valves.

Vermirovsky scored another victory in the same year, winning the Leningrad–Tiflis–Moscow long-distance race of 5300 kilometres. He was the only driver to arrive without a penalty point, and was awarded an extra prize for the durability and economy of his car.

The name Tatra was becoming so well known that in 1927 the management decided to change the factory name from Koprivnice Vozovka A.S. to Zavody Tatra A.S. (Tatra Works Ltd). At this point it was recorded that the various units of the company had produced 150,000 carts and coaches, 50,000 railway carriages and wagons, and 8000 cars and trucks. Current production capacity was 400 carriages and 4000 rolling stock for the railways, and up to 4000 cars. There were 3000 manual workers and 300 administrative staff.

Up to 1930 the form produced about 25,000 Tatra 11 and Tatra 12 models, the latter being similar to the 11 but with four-wheel brakes. A number of four-cylinder models followed, designed on similar lines to the 11 with air-cooled opposing twin cylinder engines, tubular backbone and swing axles: the 30 with 1680 cc 40 hp,

Above: Tatra's 77 model had the world's first all-enveloping stream-lined saloon body; developed from the 77 were the 77A, the 87 and 97 models

Below: the Tatra 603 was introduced in 1957 and was still in production in T603 form in 1975; the initial 603 used a 2.5-litre engine

the 52 with 1910 cc 40 hp engine, and the more significant 57 of 1932 with a flat-four engine of 1160 cc developing 22 hp, known as the Hadimrska. Variations of this lightweight model were produced by Tatra up until 1940, and it appeared in Germany as the Rohr Junior and in Vienna as the Austro–Tatra, both versions being built under licence.

At this time Tatra also produced an in-line six-cylinder Type 70 of 3400 cc producing 60 hp, and a big six-litre V12 Type 80 giving 100 hp. At the other extreme, a little 528 cc three-wheeler Type 49 was tried, but few of these little cars were produced.

Ledwinka's next major contribution to Tatra's reputation, designed in collaboration with another Tatra engineer, Ubelacker, was the Type 77 of 1934—the world's first all-enveloping streamlined body. The car had a central box-frame which forked behind the rear axle to hold a 3400 cc V8 air-cooled engine developing 70 hp and giving the 77 a top speed of 95 mph. The Tatra 77A and 87 models which followed modified and improved the design. The 87 was significant—though the engine size was reduced to 2960 cc it put out 75 hp and gave the car a 100 mph top speed because of weight reduction in the design. In the same year, 1937, that the 87 was introduced, a four-cylinder engined version was offered—the Type 97, with a flat-four unit of 1760 cc. With Koprivnice under German occupation, model policy was restricted and the 97 was discontinued. The Type 87 continued in production until 1941.

The firm was also developing trucks at this time, the three-ton T27 and T27B being manufactured from 1936. A six-and-a-half-ton T81 with three driven axles and a 120/150 hp eight-cylinder water-cooled engine was produced in 1939. Eight- and ten-ton trucks based on this followed in 1942, the latter having a 12-cylinder air-cooled diesel unit. Subsequently nearly 15,000 of these vehicles were exported to a total of 59 countries.

After World War II the Tatra works were nationalised in 1945 by the Czech government, and car production was concentrated on two types, the old front-engined 57B four-cylinder model and the rear-engined 87 eight-cylinder, though Tatra's main immediate post-war task was to replace the 60,000 railway waggons and carriages lost by Czechoslovakia.

But the firm was still the country's biggest car and truck maker, accounting for 46 per cent of car production in 1946 and 1947 and employing over 5000

workers. A new passenger car was introduced in 1948 to replace the 57B and 87—the Tatraplan T600, based on the pre-war 97 but with a two-litre engine mounted in the rear. Production of this car was transferred in 1951 from Koprivnice to the firm's AZNP Mlada Boleslav factory, in order to make way for the manufacture of T128 and T111 R trucks in quantity. (Production of railway rolling stock also ceased in the same year for the same reason.) The two trucks had identical components and were designed for off-road work, including hilly locations, the swing-axle configuration allowing higher speeds over rough ground than rigid axles. A towing tractor unit, the T141, and a T805 off-road utility one-and-a-half-tonner were also introduced.

The Tatraplan car continued in production until 1952, after which there was a three year period in which no private cars at all were made by Tatra.

But the design staff were working on a new project against the day when production would be resumed, and in 1955 Tatra started making cars again. These reached the home market in quantity from 1957. The new model was the T603, with an air-cooled V8 engine of 2472 cc mounted in the rear. Floorpan design was for the first time flat, and a new helical spring suspension gave a much improved ride compared with earlier cars.

This car remained in production until 1973 in T3-603 form with twin-carburettor engine, servo-assisted brakes and power-assisted steering. A further development, the 3.4-litre T613, followed in that year. But Tatra's main concern today is commercial vehicles and the old Nesselsdorf occupation, railway rolling stock manufacture. In 1958 came a new T805 one-and-a-half-ton truck with air-cooled eight-cylinder engine below the driver's cab. The following year the T138 was added, powered by an air-cooled V8 engine producing 192 hp, with swing axles, pneumatic gear-change and more than 20 body alternatives covering a wide variety of commercial uses.

1966 saw a new type, the T813 three-axle tipper truck with 250 hp unit, from which was developed a four-axle truck with tyres whose pressure could be varied while the vehicle was running.

From 1964 to 1966 truck production increased by 60 per cent, and 32.5 per cent of all Tatra products are exported. Since 1950 the export of all Tatra vehicles has been in the hands of Motokov, the Czech foreign trade corporation. Production had reached 7000 trucks a year in the 12–16-ton class by 1970, and since this capacity still did not meet Czechoslovakia's own needs as well as export demands, a further programme to increase capacity to 15,000 trucks was inaugurated.   EF

Top: the two-seater sports Tatra 57 of 1935

Centre: another view of Tatra's strange-looking T603 model; this is a 1968 version

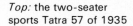

Bottom: the T613 was developed from the T603 model; it used the air-cooled V8 Tatra motor, albeit stretched to 3.4 litres

TAXIMETER CABRIOLET

Few people realise that this term is the full version of what is now shortened to a universal 'taxi', used throughout the world to hail hire cars

NOWADAYS THE TAXI-CAB is an indispensable part of transportation in major towns and cities all over the world: yet 80 years ago, it seemed as though no form of mechanical vehicle could challenge the supremacy of the horse-drawn carriage. In London alone, there were more than 11,000 horse cabs of various sorts plying for hire; in most cases the hire fees were purely arbitrary, to be agreed before the journey began.

The first challenge from the newly fledged motor vehicle came on a snowy March day in 1896 when the Stuttgart horse-cab proprietor, Dietz, convinced that

there was great potential for a motor-cab service in the city, where steep streets made horse-drawn cabs uneconomical, put a Benz on the streets for the approval of the local chief of police. Though the car was running with a hastily repaired gearbox, and the police had mapped out a particularly difficult test route, nevertheless, the driver of the car, Ignaz Axtmann, head mechanic of the Benz company, covered the course with flying colours. Dietz was granted a licence to operate two Benz cabs, which were available for hire between breakdowns.

Below: ''ere guv, what do you mean you've never been so frightened in your life? Anyway, you should do what I do, just keep your eyes closed.' The scene is London, the date is 1975 and the taxi-cab is a diesel-engined variety from Austin

The Stuttgart motor-cab company inaugurated Germany's first regular motor cab service in May 1897 using a fleet of seven rear-engined 4 hp twin-clinder Cannstatt-Daimlers delivered between September 1896 and October 1899. 'The extremely elegant vehicles are driven by experienced drivers in livery and are also available at night,' stated the publicity issued by the cab company; six passengers could be carried at one time, and the closed portion of the vehicles' landaulette bodies could be heated in cold weather. Average run for the Daimlers was 125 miles a day.

Meanwhile motor cabs had come to Paris, where Emile Roger, the local Benz agent, had launched an experimental service in 1896, and to London where the young electrical engineer, Walter Bersey, had introduced a fleet of electric motor cabs in the late summer of 1897. Forty storage batteries enabled the Bersey cabs to run for fifty miles at an average of 10 mph, but they enjoyed only limited success, despite the fulsome comments of *Black & White* magazine: 'In the convenience and comfort afforded, the electric cab is an improvement on everything that preceded it. Its spaciousness, spring seats, self-closing doors, extra windows, and, above all, the arrangement for lighting the interior with electricity, are alike excellent.'

Indeed the only claim to history that the Bersey electric cabs have is that one of them was the cause of the first fatal motor accident, when a boy, attempting to steal a ride on the rear boot of the cab was wound into its mechanism.

In Paris, too, electric cabs were early on the scene; in 1898 the Compagnie Générale des Voitures à Paris founded the world's first driving school for would-be cab drivers on a waste site at Aubervilliers. A 700-metre course was laid out on which the trainee drivers had to steer between hedges and dodge between life-size models of jay-walking pedestrians.

A contest to determine the most viable form of motor cab was organised by the Automobile Club de France from June 1–12, 1898, when eleven electric cabs and a solitary Peugeot petrol coupé were tested for reliability and regularity of running over nine radial routes of 60 kilometres each. Most of the electric vehicles were entered either by Jeantaud and Kriéger who were the two leading manufacturers of electric vehicles; not surprisingly the two marques shared most of the honours. The judges did not reckon much on the Peugeot, which they thought had no advantage other

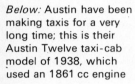

Below: Austin have been making taxis for a very long time; this is their Austin Twelve taxi-cab model of 1938, which used an 1861 cc engine

Left: an American taxi driver about to answer a call on his radio

Below: in an effort to eliminate the image of the bullying, rude New York taxi driver, the Black Pearl company issued it drivers with this message

WHAT IS A CUSTOMER?

A CUSTOMER IS THE MOST IMPORTANT PERSON EVER IN THIS ESTABLISHMENT.

A CUSTOMER IS NOT DEPENDENT UPON US, WE ARE DEPENDENT ON HIM.

A CUSTOMER IS NOT AN INTERRUPTION OF OUR WORK; HE IS THE PURPOSE OF IT. WE ARE NOT DOING HIM A FAVOR BY SERVING HIM; HE IS DOING US A FAVOR BY GIVING US AN OPPORTUNITY TO DO SO.

A CUSTOMER IS NOT AN OUTSIDE TO OUR BUSINESS; HE IS PART OF IT.

A CUSTOMER IS NOT A COLD FACTOR, HE IS A FLESH AND BLOOD HUMAN BEING, WITH BIASES, PREJUDICES, FEELINGS AND EMOTIONS, LIKE OUR OWN.

A CUSTOMER IS NOT SOMEONE TO ARGUE WITH, NOBODY EVER WON AN ARGUMENT WITH A CUSTOMER.

A CUSTOMER IS A PERSON WHO BRINGS US HIS WANTS. IT'S OUR JOB TO SERVE HIM WELL.

Black Pearl

than speed, and was in any case too heavy on petrol, especially to keep the ignition burners of its Daimler engine alight.

'Henceforth,' concluded one M. Hospitalier, who claimed to know about such things, 'it is certain that the petrol-cab cannot constitute a workable system for public transport in cities.'

Obviously inspired by such confidence in the future of electricity, Kriéger established an elaborate charging station for his electromobiles in Paris.

Electricity was the coming thing in Amrica, too, it seemed, for Riker and Morris & Salom were also building cabs powered by batteries; the poor road system outside urban areas in the USA was to favour the use of such 'homing pigeons' (so-called because of their recurrent need to return to the recharging station) for two decades to come.

London's first petrol cab, a Rational, appeared on the streets in 1903; it was a neat forward-control machine with an underfloor engine. Next year, a Hérald (which looked rather similar to the contemporary Panhard) was also in service, and by 1905 there were 19 motor cabs in London . . . and 10,361 of the horsedrawn variety.

Included among that 19 were a Vauxhall motor hansom, designed by the Earl of Ranfurly, with the driver sitting eight feet up in the air at the rear of the body, and four Fords operated by their importer, the Central Motor Car Agency. The agency's head, Percival Perry (who subsequently became the head of Ford of Britain and Lord Perry of Stock Harvard) planned to put a fleet of 200 cabs on the streets of London, but his plans were dashed when Henry Ford abandoned production of the four-cylinder Model B, on which the cabs were to be built, in favour of the little Model N 'Baby Ford', fore-runner of the Model T.

The man who eventually established the motor cab in London was Davison Dalziel, whose family was in quite a different sphere, that of wood-engraving. Dalziel founded both the United Motor Cab Company and the General Motor Cab Company, then, in July 1908, pulled off a million-pound merger between the two companies, thus obtaining control over 1200 of the 2805 motor cabs running in London. The new 7½-acre premises of the General Motor Cab Company in Brixton was virtually a self-contained taxi factory, where everything from coachwork to pneumatic tyres was made. Only the chassis—built by Renault and Darracq in France and Wolseley in England—came from an outside source.

Dalziel's drivers constituted an élite corps. In 1907 each one took an average of £2 3s 6d, of which he was permitted to keep 11s (however, he had to buy his own petrol) plus whatever tips he was given. Every driver had to undergo strict medical checks, by the cab company's own doctor, 'with special reference to the condition of his heart and lungs, his sight and hearing and his freedom from all alcoholic taint and tendency.' He had also to pass a Scotland Yard test on his knowledge of London.

This police supervision of cabbies was hardly novel, since 1829 a Metropolitan Police department had been charged with the responsibility for ensuring that the capital's cabs, both horse-drawn and self-propelled, were clean, safe, and well-maintained, and conformed to certain constructional and operational criteria before a licence could be issued.

Right: a one-horsepower cab pictured in the middle of Paris' *Champs Elysees*

Below: taxis come in all shapes and sizes; this is the one-manpower model favoured in the Far East

It was the Hackney Carriage office which stepped in when one of the six Rationals which made up London's first taxi fleet was involved in a bad-weather collision, which its driver blamed on rain obscuring the windscreen. So, to prevent a recurrence of the incident, all London taxis were promptly forbidden to have glass windscreens, a draconian measure which was only relaxed after ten years, when half-height screens were grudgingly permitted. And in the 1920s three-quarter height glass was allowed, provided that the driver slid the screen in front of his face aside in bad weather; proper windscreens were only legalised on cabs when automatic windscreen wipers became universal, hence the bloodshot eyes and hacking cough of the early cabbies. . . .

Nevertheless, the rise of the motor cab was irresistible: in 1910 there were two horse-drawn cabs for every motorised taxi, while a year later petrol was in the ascendancy, with 6336 motor cabs against a fast-dwindling 4800 of the equine variety, soon to be reduced to only a handful of hacks for the tourist trade.

The real growth of the motor cab business, however, dates from the introduction in Paris in 1903 of the taximeter, which automatically calculated the cost of the hire in terms of time and distance according to a predetermined tariff. From Paris, too, came the standard design of coachwork, a kind of cabriolet de ville inspired by the design of chauffeur-driven vehicles . . . hence the name '*taximètre cabriolet*', which has been familiarised into 'taxi-cab'.

Parisian taxi-drivers were quick to band into protective associations to counter the opposition of horse-drawn cabs—'*les fiacres hippomobiles*'—and such groupings as 'La Cooperative des Chauffeurs', 'Le Syndicat des Cochers Chauffeurs' and 'L'Association des Cochers Automobiles' formed the basis for financial combines of cab operators. In May 1905, one such operating group, the Compagnie des Fiacres de Paris, ordered 1500 Renault 8 hp twin-cylinder cabs, which entered service in the following December, 'sweet little motor carriages that are so cute that their status as cabs is only revealed by their taximeter.'

The biggest cab company in Paris, the Compagnie Parisienne des Automobiles de Place, countered by ordering a fleet of Clément-Bayards equipped with heated passenger compartments.

In the summer of 1908, the Automobile Club de France organised a month-long trial of taxicabs, during which the competitors had to cover a distance of 4000 km. The unfortunate passengers who hailed the cabs competing in the trials stood a fair chance of ending up somewhere completely different from their intended destination!

The results of the trial, not unexpectedly, were victories in their respective categories for the two most popular models, the 8 hp twin-cylinder Renault and the 10/16 hp four-cylinder Clément-Bayard.

But three years later a steep rise in taxi fares provoked an immediate reaction from the Parisian public, stirred to anger by press articles: the taxis were boycotted, and stood empty in long rows on their ranks until the charges were reduced to a compromise level. And by the outbreak of war, the taxi service was operating perfectly, a fact which was amply demonstrated when the German Army under Von Kluck marched on Paris in September 1914.

Only 25 km separated the Germans from the French capital, and an advanced column was already making dangerous inroads into the French position on the Marne. Reinforcements had to be brought into the front line at once, but when 12,000 troops of the 103rd Regiment arrived in Paris on September 7 with orders to be at Nanteuil le Hardin at 8 o'clock the following morning, the railway could only take 6000 of them. So the newly appointed Military Governor of Paris, Joseph-Simon Galliéni, commandeered 600 cabs, mainly Renaults, to carry the remaining troops to the battlefront.

About 6 o'clock that evening, each cab, carrying five *poilus*, set out for the front, watched by Gallieni from the comfort of a vast Mors tourer. The convoy, accompanied by trucks carrying spare tyres, made two trips . . . and Paris was saved.

The cab company charged the army the fare shown on the meter, and the cost of replacement tyres, while each driver received a 30 per cent tip of around 35 francs. It was a combination of patriotism and sound financial sense which appealed to the French spirit, and the 'Taxis de la Marne' passed into French mythology.

Renault continued to build specially designed taxis for Paris for many years afterwards, notably the KZII model based on the 13.9 Vivaquatre chassis and manufactured especially for the Compagnie Autoplace, of which 2400 were in service between 1932 and 1962, during which time some covered over 500,000 miles.

In America, taxi-cab operation became big business when a young Austrian immigrant, John Hertz, who had run away from home at the age of 12 and held a variety of jobs, solved the problem of what to do with the second-hand cars traded-in to his car sales company in exchange for new Berliets.

'As my customers weren't buyers of second-hand cars, I had to put on my thinking cap to find some way of disposing of them or making them earn their keep,' recalled Hertz. 'Having driven a delivery wagon, I figured that there should be money in the passenger delivery business. Joy-riding was beginning to become popular. Families were taking to hiring a car for outings, especially on Sundays. And a few taxis were beginning to make their appearance.'

In 1914, Hertz managed to raise $50,000 to start a taxi fleet, and commissioned a local university to find out what was the most distinctive colour that would stand out most strongly to a prospective passenger at a distance: the result was a bright yellow—hence the foundation of the Yellow Cab Company.

From the start, Hertz chose courteous and efficient drivers, whom he paid above-average wages: he also undercut all other taxi operators. Hertz eventually set up a nationwide network of Yellow Cab franchise companies, and even built his own cabs: by the early 1920s some 6000 were in service in New York alone. Throughout the USA at this period, Yellow Taxis carried over 145,000,000 passengers, earned an income of $142,000,000 and covered 612,000,000 miles.

By 1929, however, Hertz had ceased making his own cabs, and since then standard makes have been used. More consistent has been the record of the Checker Corporation of Kalamazoo, Michigan, which since 1923 has specialised in the manufacture of taxi-cabs, only branching out into 'pleasure cars' as a sideline in 1959.

Since the demise of the old pre-Great War Renaults and Charrons, the British taxicab industry has been largely dominated by Austin, whose heavy 12 cab of the 1930s, with its regulation landaulette body, epitomised the London Taxi to most people. Its supremacy has been challenged by such makes as Beardmore and the Ford Cortina-engined Winchester, but it is still the Austin cab which dominates the London streets. And, because of the necessarily limited market, it seems likely that it will continue to do so as long as Scotland Yard dictates the shape of London's taxis. DBW

Below: a typical New York street scene, complete with skyscrapers, buses, advertising hoardings and yellow taxi-cabs

FROM GO-KARTS TO FORMULA ONE

The Pederzani brothers have had a chequered career in motor racing with their Tecno cars and engines

THE BOLOGNA-BASED Tecno firm started off building tiny karts and quickly moved up-market to produce small-capacity racing cars. Their Formula Three and Formula Two machines helped foster the racing careers of top drivers such as Clay Regazzoni, François Cevert, Ronnie Peterson and Reine Wisell. In 1972, they made the mistake of entering Grand Prix racing on a tight budget, attempting to emulate Ferrari by building their own 3-litre flat-12 engine. After two seasons, the Pederzani brothers, the proprietors of Tecno (and of a successful hydraulic pump-making factory whose profits largely financed the racing efforts), were forced to withdraw from Formula One and, it seemed, the entire motor-racing scene. They did have a 2-litre flat-8 engine available for sports-car racing, but no one willing to finance its development.

Luciano and Gianfranco Pederzani, born in 1926 and 1942 respectively, designed and built the first successful Italian karts in 1962, because Luciano, who raced these nimble 'motorised roller-skates', felt his country should be represented in this international sport. Tecno karts won the World Championship for four successive years (1963 to 1966), and over the years around 20,000 were constructed at the tiny works, un-named at the end of a dirt road on the outskirts of Bologna.

It was logical to progress to motor racing, the Italian 250 cc Formula Four class being supported from 1964 to 1968 when approximately 230 Tecno K250s were built, the majority with Ducati engines. Several were campaigned in Britain, although the formula was poorly supported. The next stage up the ladder was an 850 cc Fiat-engined single-seater for Formula 850, an Italian national formula. One car was built, a space-frame design with an unusually forward seating position. It was really a prototype for international Formula Three which, in those days, was for cars with 1-litre production engines (the Ford unit was almost universally used). The first example was entered in an unusually tough event, the Circuit of Mugello, basically a sports-car event, but which in July of 1966 had a separate class for Formula Three cars. Driven by Carlo Facetti, the Tecno TF66/3-Ford finished fourth, despite braking and suspension problems, behind two De Sanctis and a BWA; later, he was third at Monza. Facetti, Giancarlo Baghetti and Clay Regazzoni were entered for the 1967 Argentine Temporada in improved Tecno TF67/3-Fords. The seating positions did cause problems inasmuch as the drivers found their mounts difficult to control and the cars were out of contention, but revisions made prior to the European season transformed the Tecno's handling: it became a potential winner.

Tecno's reputation was made by Regazzoni: the forceful Swiss driver put up many impressive performances, but reliability was a problem and it was not until late in the year when Tecno's name appeared on the results lists. Regazzoni was second in the European Formula Three Trophy at Hockenheim in October and

Above right: the 2-litre flat-eight Tecno sports-car engine of 1974 was a development of Tecno's unsuccessful flat-twelve Formula One engine

Below: the prototype Formula One Tecno PA123 was introduced in December 1971; it was of space-frame construction and used the Pederzani flat-twelve 2967 cc engine

in November's end-of-season race at Jarama in Spain, he won, beating many top Formula Three drivers. These results boosted Tecno's image, and competitors reckoned a Tecno was *the* car to have. The Pederzani brothers were inundated with orders for 1968, among their customers being Swedish stars Ronnie Peterson and Reine Wisell and up-and-coming Frenchman François Cevert. No fewer than 43 TF68/3 chassis were sold; a Formula Two version was also planned, ten of these being built.

Tecno's many customers gave the Italian company a tremendous boost: in Formula Three over thirty international wins were accrued, chiefly by Wisell and Peterson. Among other Tecno pilots in Formula Three were Briton Chris Craft with his ex-works Tecno TF67/3 and Gijs van Lennep and Mike Beckwith who

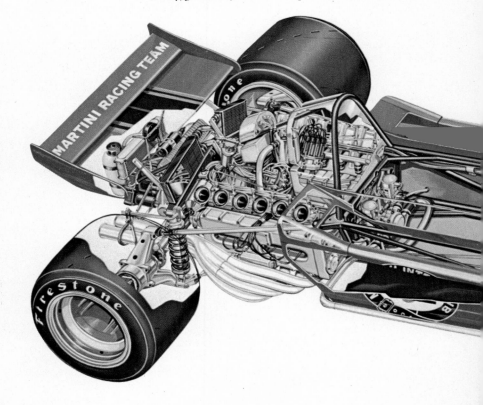

drove the Tecno-DAFs which used the Dutch firm's belt-drive automatic transmission. On the engine side, Tecno developed their own version of the Cosworth-Ford MAE which proved very powerful.

The Formula Two Tecno TF68/2, a strengthened version of the Formula Three car to cope with the extra power of the 1600 cc Cosworth-Ford FVA engine, was not so successful, suffering in the steering, handling and braking departments. Regazzoni contested the European Formula Two Trophy, finishing third at Crystal Palace, fourth at Enna and fifth at Jarama. The Ron Harris team equipped themselves with Tecnos, Dickie Attwood taking a third at Zandvoort and Pedro Rodriguez a fourth at Hockenheim; private entrant Silvio Moser followed Attwood home at Zandvoort. In December's Argentine Temporada, Jo Siffert joined the team, taking a fourth at Zonda and a third at Buenos Aires, to finish seventh in the championship.

For 1969, Tecno decided to contentrate on the development of the Formula Two car, and did not sell any to private owners (apart from one older-specification model to Briton Alistair Walker); works team drivers were François Cevert and Nanni Galli. Finance for the Formula Two team largely came from the sale of karts and Formula Three machines, well over 70 TF69/3s being sold in 1969. Rumours of a Ford DFV-engined Formula One Tecno financed by Ron Harris and to be driven by Pedro Rodriguez came to nothing when Harris ran into financial difficulties early in the year. Looking ahead, Gianfranco Pederzani thought Tecno might eventually develop a sports car.

Cevert gained Tecno their first Formula Two victory at Rheims in a typical slipstreaming battle at the French circuit. With thirds at Monza and Enna, plus fifths at Pau and Tulln-Langenlebarn, Cevert finished third in the European Formula Two Trophy. In Formula

Three, Tecno once more earned over thirty wins, Peterson being the most successful and winning the Swedish title for the second successive year.

Fewer cars were sold and fewer successes were gained in Formula Three in 1970. Jean-Pierre Jaussaud won the French Championship, taking his 1969-model Tecno TF69/3 to victory at Nogaro, Pau, Paul Ricard, Magny-Cours and Montlhéry, but even he deserted Tecno's ranks at the end of the year. The Italian, Giovanni Salvati, was proclaimed Italian Champion; he won at Monza (twice), Imola, Hockenheim and Magny-Cours. Other winners included Hermann Unold, Jean Johansson and Jean-Pierre Jarier. In Formula Two, however, Clay Regazzoni's Motul-sponsored works car presented him with the European Trophy.

Encouraged by their success, Tecno announced ambitious plans for 1971. In addition to production cars (Formula Fords and American Formula B models were built as well as Formula Threes), they were to be represented by two Formula Two teams, develop their own version of Ford's BDA engine using FVA parts in anticipation of the new Formula Two scheduled for the following year and begin work on a Formula One car of their own. This was *not* to feature the ubiquitous Cosworth-Ford DFV engine, but a flat-12 unit of Tecno's very own.

The Elf petrol company backed the official works team of Formula Two Tecno TF71/2s with three French drivers, François Cevert, Jean-Pierre Jabouille and Patrick Depailler. The cars were further developed with inboard rear brakes, but basically they were little changed from the original space-frame design of 1967. The 1970 works cars were sold to the Italian Ceramiche-Iris team for a selection of drivers which included Arturo Merzario, Nanni Galli, Claudio Fran-

Above: the Formula Two Tecno TF71/2 of 1971; this car used a Tecno-modified Ford BDA engine. In F2, however, Tecno never enjoyed the success that their F3 cars earned and, indeed, 1971 was to prove a particularly frustrating year for Tecno F2 drivers

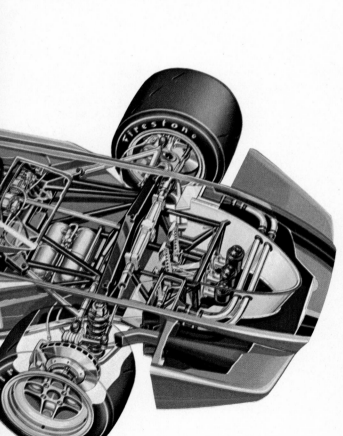

cisci and Gianluigi Fontanesi. Cevert began the season brilliantly with victories at Hockenheim, Nürburgring and Vallelunga, but thereafter the Tecno-developed Ford BDA engines suffered from unreliability owing to badly made parts from outside suppliers, and Cevert fell from first to an eventual fifth place in the European Trophy. His team-mates fared as badly, Jabouille's second at Pau being the only good result of significance. The Ceramiche-Iris Tecno TF70/2s were very badly prepared and suffered as a result. In Formula Three, lack of development told and few international successes were gained.

At first promised for the end of the 1971 season, Tecno's prototype Formula One car was unveiled in December. First plans called for the construction of five cars, one for Italian Nanni Galli, another for 'a driver bringing outside sponsorship to the team' and three as spares or development models. In fact, Martini International agreed to sponsor the works team and ex-Vanwall and JW team manager David Yorke was brought in by Martini to co-ordinate the various interests, and he signed Briton Derek Bell as the second driver. The prototype was of space-frame construction—indeed, it was built on the same jigs as the Formula Two cars—and used the Pederzani brothers' new seven-bearing flat-12 engine of 2967 cc.

The Tecno PA123, as the Formula One car was named, was initially built contrary to FIA regulations. It was 30 cm too wide so that, among other modifications, the pannier fuel tanks had to be moved inwards. Early tests also revealed engine lubrication problems which were later cured by Castrol supplying special oil. A four-bearing version of the engine was eventually used in the car when it made its much-delayed début in the Belgian Grand Prix. Driven by Nanni Galli, it showed good speed, but handled terribly; he retired after spinning and being hit by Clay

Below: Derek Bell in action at the Nürburgring during the 1972 German Grand Prix; he was driving the F1 Tecno PA123/01, sponsored by the Martini Racing Team. Bell retired on lap 5. This car is the monocoque version of the spaceframe prototype shown on a previous page

Regazzoni's Ferrari. A second chassis, of neater appearance and of monocoque construction, was driven by Galli into third place in the non-championship Vallelunga race, but Bell was forced to withdraw from the French Grand Prix when sheared chassis bolts were discovered on the car. Ex-Brabham designer Ron Tauranac assisted with rear-suspension modifications prior to the British Grand Prix, but still the handling problems were not overcome, with Galli crashing early in the race. In Germany, with new Tauranac-inspired front suspension, Bell opined that the chassis was basically at fault and was relieved to retire when the engine failed. Galli suffered a variety of problems in Austria, but finished the race, while in Italy, the only time both drivers were at the same meeting, failure resulted once more. Galli, in a new chassis with revised suspension geometry and a lower frontal area, blew up and Bell's car was so badly prepared it failed to qualify to start. In Canada, Bell's car had chassis failure plus an accident which prevented him from starting, while in the United States (where the chassis was strengthened locally), the Tecno again retired early with a blown head gasket.

If the 1972 season was bad (Formula Two plans were eventually abandoned in order to concentrate on the Grand Prix car), then 1973 was a disaster! Chris Amon was invited by David Yorke to race a new car. The Pederzanis decided to concentrate on engine development and, after preliminary talks with Ron Tauranac, Chevron's Derek Bennett and ex-BRM designer Tony Southgate, agreed that ex-Lotus and McLaren mechanic (and designer of the Formula Two Tui) Alan McCall should build them a chassis. He did, but quit the team before any testing could be done owing to a disagreement. Martini also commissioned Gordon Fowell of Goral to design a chassis, the result being two completely different cars available. What attracted Amon to the team was the Tecno engine: it had shown terrific speed on occasions during 1972. In 1973, however, redesign work resulted in a substantial loss of power and, although handling problems were now overcome, the car lacked speed. Additionally, political rows between the Pederzanis and Martini did nothing to enhance the team's chances. The McCall-designed car, Tecno PA123/6, made a belated first appearance in Belgium where Amon was sixth, completing the race in a semi-conscious state owing to the car's severe overheating. Overheating sidelined the car at Monaco, where Amon qualified twelfth fastest in practice then, after missing two races, Tecno appeared at Silverstone with two cars. The Goral-designed car, Tecno E731, was briefly tried in practice and the McCall machine retired with low fuel pressure after racing in a solid last place. Similar problems caused Amon to retire the McCall car in Holland, he missed Germany and non-started in Austria after engine problems with both cars. Not surprisingly, the team withdrew from all further races.

Tecno sought further backing for 1974 but failed to attract a sponsor. They built a 2-litre flat-8 engine (actually a development of a blown-up flat-12!) for sports-car racing and arranged to supply an engine for a Lola T292 to be financed by a British team and raced by Chris Craft. Delays caused the deal to fall flat, although in July the Pederzani brothers entered the Italian Santamonica 2-litre sports-car race. The Tecno-engined Lola, driven by Jean-Pierre Jaussaud, was quickest in practice, but overheated and lost power. The car was also poorly prepared, being tended by mechanics from the Pederzanis' hydraulic-pump factory! A flat battery and overheating caused the car's eventual retirement, and it was not seen again.   MK

MEASUREMENT TO A DEGREE

Outside-air temperature and engine temperature are both important to the running of a car

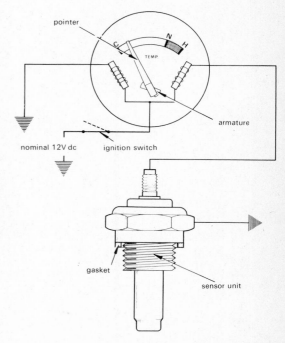

THERE ARE THREE temperatures of interest to the motorist; that of the water in the cooling system, that of the engine lubricating oil and that of the outside air.

Two types of gauge are common today: the mechanical and the electrical. In the mechanical gauge, the sensing element is a metal bulb, containing a fluid that has a high coefficient of expansion and a low freezing point, connected by a capillary tube directly to a diaphragm or Bourdon tube. When heated, the fluid expands, causing the gauge pointer, connected to the diaphragm or tube, to move across a short scale. An amplifying mechanical linkage can be included in the instrument case so that a longer, circular scale can be employed.

The electrical gauge uses a thermister bead, also mounted in a metal bulb, as the sensing element, or transmitter. The thermister is a device with a variable electrical resistance, determined by the ambient temperature: when cold, its resistance is high; when hot, its resistance is low. The vehicle's battery provides power to operate the gauge, when the ignition is switched on. The indicating meter is of either the common moving-coil or the bimetal-strip type.

One of the earliest types of water temperature gauge was a thermometer mounted in perhaps the easiest and most visible position at that time—on the radiator cap.

A later type, still used today and suitable for both oil and water temperature measurement, employs a bimetal-strip device, enclosed within a heating coil, for both the transmitter and the dashboard indicator. When the engine is first switched on, the battery alone heats the coil; the mean battery current is therefore maximum and the indicator metal strip warms up, moving the pointer, to which it is attached, to the cold position. As the engine temperature increases, the water (or oil) has its own heating effect on the transmitter

Above right: an outside air-temperature gauge, manufactured by Smiths and calibrated in both centigrade and fahrenheit; the most useful feature of this type of gauge is that it will warn a driver when the temperature is low enough for ice to be present

Below right: a diagram showing the layout of an electrical temperature gauge

Below: front and back of an instrument cluster incorporating speedometer, fuel gauge and temperature gauge; the last two are electrically operated and all connections are made, via a printed circuit, to a single plug

bimetal strip, so that less and less current is drawn from the battery. Thus there is less heating of the indicator bimetal strip, which cools, moving the pointer towards the hot position.

The most important temperature to know is that of the cooling-system water. Accurate measurement, however, is not required; calibration is often no more than 'Cold' rising to 'Hot', with the normal operating temperature (80 to 85°C) somewhere between the two. The sensing element is usually fitted near the top of the cylinder block or in the thermostat housing.

Since it is essential that a driver be aware of any unusually high water temperature, most water-cooled vehicles are fitted with a cooling-system gauge. A high reading could indicate any of the following faults: fan belt broken or slipping (on belt-driven fans); electric drive failed (on electric fans); radiator blocked inside (loose scale, for example) or outside (leaves, insects etc); collapsed radiator hose; cylinder block furred; shortage of water in the system; failure of water pump or thermostat; failure to remove radiator muff or raise blind.

Very hot weather, especially in 'stop-start' traffic, may also produce a high gauge reading, but the gauge

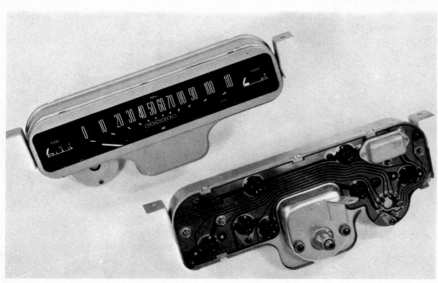

Right and below: two views of a Yazaki water-temperature gauge, of the type operated via a capillary tube rather than an electrical circuit; the sensing bulb is screwed into one of the engine's water passages and as the engine heats up, the fluid in the bulb and in the tube expands and causes the needle to move

should return to normal under cooler conditions.

After a cold start, the pointer should indicate normal operating temperature within about ten minutes. If the sensing element is installed in the thermostat housing or the radiator header tank, a 'Cold' reading should be obtained until the engine is at or near its operating temperature, when the thermostat suddenly opens.

A constantly low reading may indicate a faulty thermostat, gauge or sensing element.

Any suggestion of rising oil temperature, especially if coupled with falling oil pressure, is an alarm signal not to be ignored. A failing oil pump, shortage of oil, blockage or a 'run' bearing, all very serious defects, can cause the oil temperature to rise dramatically. However, such is the reliability of modern 'family car' engines that only a warning light, set to operate when the oil pressure has dropped to the safety limit, is normally provided. The oil temperature gauge with an informative scale is normally confined to sports, high-performance and racing cars.

Although such a gauge is rarely fitted in a mass-produced vehicle, knowledge of the outside air temperature (OAT) can be advantageous, especially at night, when the temperature may drop below zero quite unexpectedly. Awareness that freezing conditions are approaching alerts the motorist to adjust his driving technique to meet them.

The OAT guage is also of value in the higher sector of its scale, since it enables the driver to determine when the radiator muff or blind should be opened or when carburettor-air winter/summer settings should be adjusted.

Transistorised circuits, described in the electronic journals, have the conventional meter replaced by a flashing light, adjusted to operate at or near freezing temperature.

When installing all capillary type gauges, or maintaining a vehicle with one fitted, it is of vital importance that the capillary tube is not cut, kinked, twisted or disconnected from either the bulb or the gauge. Surplus tube must be loosely coiled, and there must be coils between the engine and the first attachment to the chassis, to allow the engine mountings to flex without putting strain on the capillary tubing. The manufacturer's fitting instructions must be followed in detail.

When fitting a water temperature gauge, if neither the cylinder block nor the thermostat housing is tapped to receive a transmitter element, the header tank of the radiator or one of the hoses are about the only practicable locations, although it may be possible to buy a special thermostat housing.

When fitting an oil temperature gauge, the transmitter bulb should be installed fairly low down in the side of the sump. If no tapping is provided, it is essential to ask the manufacturer of the vehicle exactly where the transmitter may be located.

The sensing element for an outside air temperature gauge is installed low down at the front of the car, since the temperature of the air nearest to the road surface is of the greatest importance. The usual location is behind the front bumper, but clear of any influence of the radiator and protected from rain or surface water spray which may produce a super-cooling effect by evaporation.

AGH

A motoring wizard from Wales

JOHN GODFREY PARRY THOMAS was perhaps the most original automotive thinker of his time. Born in 1885, Thomas had designed an advanced petrol-electric transmission which gave an infinite number of gear ratios between zero and direct top, before he was twenty-two. The Thomas Transmission, which won the Dewar Trophy in 1911, was fitted successfully to two Pipe cars and a Delahaye, although it was really intended for commercial and railway vehicles. Among the vehicles to which it was fitted (which included lorries, trams and London buses) was a railcar destined for South America, built by Leyland Motors Ltd of Leyland, Lancashire.

This company carried out a good deal of work for Thomas, who soon established a close friendship with Henry Spurrier, Junior, the son of the general manager. This association with Leyland took a new turn in 1917, when Thomas was appointed Leyland's chief engineer at the age of thirty-two.

After war-time aero-engine work, which included developing a 350 bhp power-unit with the cylinders set in 'X' formation, and light enough to be lifted by two men, Thomas was given *carte blanche* to develop the world's finest luxury car. This was the Leyland Eight, which caused a sensation when it was first exhibited at the 1920 Olympia Motor Show.

An eight-cylinder 40 hp monster with a swept volume of just under 7 litres (increased on production cars to 7266 cc by lengthening the stroke), the car had a single overhead camshaft driven from the rear of the crankshaft by triple eccentrics. The inlet and exhaust valve in each cylinder shared a common cam and a common leaf-valve spring—a typical Thomas design idiosyncracies. Aluminium plates covered the sides of the engine and made it as architecturally clean as the coping on a churchyard wall.

The chassis bristled with unconventional features—torsion-bar-assisted rear suspension, servo-assisted brakes, the gearbox located on leather cradles and a cambered rear axle. Due to a combination of circumstances no more than eighteen of these cars were built, and production ceased by the end of 1922. Some months earlier, at Easter, Parry Thomas had begun racing a two-seater Leyland Eight at Brooklands, and as the season wore on, his record of successes had become more constant. When Leyland dropped the Eight, Thomas resigned and moved into 'The Hermitage', Captain Alastair Miller's old bungalow inside the track at Brooklands. With him went several complete unsold chassis and spare parts. Over the years Thomas developed and refined his car until it bore little resemblance to the 'Lion of Olympia'; eventually it lapped Brooklands at a hairsbreadth under 130 mph. A sister car was built for Captain J. E. P. Howey, founder of the Romney, Hythe & Dymchurch Railway and perhaps the only Brooklands driver to have a pub named after him.

Parry Thomas started work on a new project in 1925. He conceived a car that would be no mere adaptation of existing parts and proprietary components, but a vehicle constructed with one idea in mind—'speed, and speed alone'. From time to time speculation appeared in the motoring press as to the form that the new car would take, but nothing concrete was published until February 1926, when work was fairly well advanced.

The chassis, low-slung and immensely strong, resembled a sledge tapered to a point at the tail. Both axles passed above the frame, the front axle being carried on semi-elliptic springs.

Thomas had recently tried out a Bugatti on Brooklands and been exceptionally impressed with it, and consequently his new car—nicknamed the 'Flat Iron'—had some echoes of Bugatti—the reversed quarter elliptic rear springs, and a gearbox, married to a multiplate clutch of under seven inches diameter, designed for rapid down changes. That is, provided the driver had mastered the idiosyncratic gear gate, for first was right and forward, while to engage second the stubby gear lever had to be

Below: John Godfrey Parry Thomas at the wheel of the famous *Babs*

moved left across the gate, and back. Third was forward from this position, and top was located across the gate again, and back, opposite first. This was probably so that, when racing at Brooklands, Thomas could go straight into top once the car was moving.

The most unorthodox feature of a thoroughly unorthodox car was without doubt the engine, described by one authority as a 'big engine with small cylinders'. There was no cylinder block as such, just water jackets, cast in pairs, hourglass-shaped in plan, with fairly exiguous water passages surrounding the steel cylinder liners.

The engine was designed as a kind of metallic sandwich, with the aluminium cylinders between the cast-iron crankcase and cylinder head. The cylinders were spigoted into the crankcase, and the head was pulled down on to them by turnbuckles threaded left and right, and drilled to take a tommy-bar. Other than these turnbuckles, there was no means of positively locating the head. A train of gears in an aluminium tower rose up into the rear of the head to drive the single overhead camshaft, which in typically Thomas fashion operated one inlet and exhaust valve per cam. Thomas did intend to fit a second camshaft under the first to give desmodromic valve operation, but never got around to it. Each pair of valves, of course, shared a leaf spring; valve clearances were variable by differential threaded micro-adjuster in the valve stem. Most of the space in the hemispherical combustion

Above: Babs, restored apart from bodywork; the Liberty-engined vehicle was buried at Pendine after its fatal crash, but was in remarkably good condition when dug out over fifty years later

chambers was taken up by the valves, and a tiny hole was all that could be seen of the ignition arrangements. Here Thomas did himself proud. The 11 mm diameter sparking plugs were a push fit in tubes passing through the water-jacket to an 'ignition hole' in each cylinder, and were thus watercooled. Specially made for Thomas by KLG, these plugs have no modern equivalent.

The two Thomas-Specials completed were run in a number of forms, supercharged and unsupercharged, with one, two or four carburettors of various sizes. Even the Roots supercharger was unorthodox, for its casing was water-cooled.

Externally, the Thomas-Special was perhaps the most striking vehicle to appear at Brooklands in the 1920s, for it was so low-slung that the only part of the coachwork higher than the wheels was the fairing of the cockpit, which was offset to the left.

The flat underside of the frame formed an unbroken streamline, and the driver's seat was a mere five inches above the track. In fact, the head resistance of the Thomas-Special was reduced to such a low figure that Thomas' assistant, Reid Railton, estimated that an output of 60 bhp would be enough to propel the car at 100 mph.

Parry Thomas' career was tragically curtailed in March 1927 when he was decapitated by a broken driving chain while attempting to recapture the Land Speed Record in his V-12 27-litre Liberty aero-engined *Babs*. Ironically, Thomas had a live-axle conversion for *Babs* on the drawing board at the time of his death.

Two cars and three engines had been laid down, one engine being destined for a racing motorboat which never materialised; but their performance potential was never fully realised, and after Thomas's death, one of the cars suffered the ignominy of being fitted with a Perkins diesel for record breaking.

Of all the advanced projects for which Parry Thomas was responsible, little now remains. The Leyland-Thomas racing cars were destroyed during the war, and *Babs* was buried near the scene of the fatal disaster on Pendine Sands but has recently been disinterred and restored. The only surviving Leyland Eight was assembled from spare parts after Thomas' death by his friends and associates Thompson and Taylor at Brooklands. A couple of racing cars have Hooker-Thomas engines built by the Walthamstowe firm of Peter Hooker and originally intended for taxicabs, but fitted to Brooklands racers instead. One of the Flat-Irons survives, and some parts of a 750 cc racing car which was never completed. Plus a bed which this shy bachelor, famed for his fairisle pullovers, endowed to the Great Ormond Street Children's Hospital. DBW

BRAINCHILD OF A NON-DRIVER

The irony of the Thomas Flyer company was that it was fostered by a man who had never actually learned to drive a motor car

THE THOMAS COMPANY was founded in Buffalo, New York in 1900 by Edwin Ross Thomas, who had previously been involved in the Railway business. He bought part of the moribund Globe Cycle Company, and began building bicycles and motor cycles. In 1902, car production began in a new factory at 1200 Niagara Street; the first model was a light single-cylinder car, joined soon after by a twin-cylinder and in 1903 by a three-cylinder car with a De Dion-type bonnet.

The three-cylindered Thomas, rated at 24 hp, acquired a conventional radiator and bonnet at the end of 1903 with a Roi des Belges body. This car, the first to bear the name 'Thomas-Flyer' cost $2500. A limousine version with a detachable hardtop cost $3000.

In 1905, the range consisted of 40 hp four, a 50 hp four and a 60 hp six, all big chain-driven models with prices ranging from $3000 to $7000. A feature of several models that year was an all-metal side-entrance tonneau-body 'made on patented dust-proof lines', with a luggage cupboard built into the back of the driving seat. The 60 hp six-cylinder Thomas Flyer was available, apart from the standard seven-passenger touring or limousine coachwork, as a two-seated racer.

A racing 60 hp six was, indeed, entered for the Vanderbilt Cup Eliminating Trials on Long Island,

driven by Montague Roberts, but this bore no resemblance to the catalogue version. It was a freakish machine in which the bonnet and scuttle occupied the entire wheelbase while the driver and mechanic were seated behind the rear axle.

The Thomas came through the Trials with apparent success, and seemed all set to take part in the Vanderbilt Cup as one of the official American entries. But two days afterwards the Cup Race Commission decided to set aside the results of the Eliminating Trials and threw out the Thomas, the Royal and the Haynes, which had been selected for the team. Instead the team selected a White Steamer, a Pope-Toledo and a front-wheel-drive Christie. In the actual race, the Pope and the White broke down on the fourth lap after the Christie had crashed in the third: whether the Thomas could have bettered this showing is a matter for conjecture.

The 1906 Thomases had thoroughly Europeanised look, with radiators closely copied from the De Dion Bouton pattern; it was rumoured that E. R. Thomas had imported Richard-Brasier parts and patterns from France and copied them exactly as a model for the mechanical components of his cars.

About this time, E. R. Thomas was on holiday in

Above: a 1908 Thomas-Flyer-Tourer; the Thomas Flyer appelation was applied to all the Thomas Company's autos after 1905

Above: the 1907 K-6-70 six-cylinder, 72 hp car that won the gruelling New York–Paris race in 1908; this car is now a priceless exhibit at William Harrah's auto mobile collection in Reno, Nevada

California when he met a twenty-six-year-old sales manager from Oldsmobile, Roy D. Chapin, who was seeking finance to enable him to set up in business as a manufacturer, producing medium-priced quality cars to the design of his colleague Howard E. Coffin. Thomas agreed to help back the venture, and the Thomas-Detroit Company was founded, building cars in a small match factory belonging to Louis Mendelssohn, who subsequently became the financial backer of the Fisher Body Company. The first year's production of this new model totalled 506 cars, but Chapin wasn't satisfied. Though the Thomas-Detroit was priced lower than the parent make, at $2750 he felt it was still too costly. So he persuaded Thomas to sell his majority holding in the company to Hugh Chalmers in 1907 and changed the name of the company to Chalmers-Detroit, which was eventually taken over by Maxwell and then became part of Chrysler.

Meanwhile the parent company was expanding. According to the company's chief road tester, George Schuster, output in 1907 was 700 cars and 400 taxicabs. Each car produced had to prove itself capable of climbing Brewery Hill in Buffalo in top gear, and of achieving 55 to 60 mph on the road before being handed over to the customer. Car output rose to 816 in 1908 in which year one of the 1907 model 60 hp four-cylinder Thomas-Flyers was entered for the strenuous 20,000 mile New York to Paris Race. The old model had been chosen because the 1908 cars were not such good hill climbers as the previous year's production and were suffering from teething troubles. The car entered for the race was a standard 1907 Roadster with few modifications except for planks strapped to the mudguards and a non-standard front axle to give increased ground clearance, plus of course extra petrol and oil storage. Despite recurrent transmission trouble, the Thomas was judged winner of the race by 26 days, having taken 169 days for the journey across three continents. The result was the subject of much controversy for a German-entered Protos had arrived in Paris some days earlier, but had then been penalised for having been taken part of the way by train.

However, the Thomas company failed to take sufficient advantage of their victory in this longest-ever motor race, for immediately after the event they issued a laughably mendacious publicity booklet which claimed that throughout the race the Thomas-Flyer 'was never in a repair shop . . . none of the valves were ground or changed; not a spark plug was changed; nor were the crankshaft bearings changed or adjusted.' As the mechanical upsets of the Thomas had received reasonably wide publicity, the booklet was shown up as a fraud. There was *some* marketing spin-off gained from the race victory, however, and for a while the Thomas Company was working night and day to produce cars, taxicabs, and fire engines.

The following year production reached its all-time peak of 1906 after which it fell to 913 in 1910. Much of the blame for this down-turn in sales can be credited to the poor reliability record of the Thomas Model L Flyabout, the company's first shaft-driven car which was noisy, under-powered and suffered from catastrophic oil leaks. Staff salaries were reduced in 1910, and E. R. Thomas, who in his decade in the motor industry had never learnt to drive a car, sold his interest in the company to a New York banking comany, Eugene M. Meyer, who in the following year appointed a new board composed of former Packard executives who had resigned from that company when Alvan Macauley had taken over. But the new team was too late to save Thomas, which went into receivership on 29 August 1912, with assets of $1,700,000 and liabilities of $960,000. Under the then current company laws this was sufficient ground for the company to be declared bankrupt, and its assets were auctioned off in March 1913 for a paltry $256,000. Among the assets auctioned off was the round-the-world race winner, which was included in a job lot of vehicles, parts, patents and good-will; this historic car rusted in the garage of a Buffalo publisher for many years, was unearthed in the 1940s and is now part of William Harrah's four-figure collection of early vehicles at Reno, Nevada.

Thomas-Flyer cars were apparently available to special order until 1919, but it seems likely that these were merely assembled from the stockpile of parts disposed of at the company sale in 1913. E. R. Thomas himself died while visiting his brother in Buffalo in 1936, at the age of 85.   DBW

Man of speed

AMERICAN MICKEY THOMPSON was a man of speed. In his years at the forefront of the automotive world he could not resist a challenge. He was a racing driver, a drag-racing exponent, a record-breaker and a builder of racing cars designed to win the Indianapolis 500. He may not have been successful in everything he attempted, but Thompson sought and attained the type of publicity usually reserved for winners. During his twenty years at the wheel of many different types of car he established 485 international, national and American class records.

Marian Lee 'Mickey' Thompson, son of a detective, was born on 7 December 1928, in San Fernando, California. Before he was old enough to hold an official driving licence he restored early Fords and Chevrolets and in his mid-teens he also began participating in drag-racing and hot-rod events.

In 1953 Thompson competed in the *Carrera Panamericana*—the Mexican road race—and ran his Ford over a cliff attempting to avoid a cluster of spectators. His forté was drag racing, though. In 1955 he became the first man to exceed 120 mph on a quarter-mile strip, and by the time the year was out he had raised the figure to 150 mph. With a twin-engined machine, he cracked the American land-speed record in 1958, leaving it at 294 mph. His next aim was the world record of 394.2 mph set by Briton John Cobb in 1947. Thompson's *Challenger I*, a fearsome machine powered by four 6.8-litre Pontiac V8 engines running on a mixture of alcohol and nitro, raised the American figure to 330.51 mph; he beat Cobb's record in one direction only (at 406.60 mph); a broken drive-shaft prevented a return run. Later an engine failed and subsequently an accident and a disagreement with his sponsor meant *Challenger I* was not seen again.

In 1959 Thompson cracked several international class records. He raised the 5-km figure to 345.33 mph, the 5-mile to 340.70 mph, the 10-km to 327.59 mph and the 10-mile to 286.16 mph. A year later, with a Pontiac-engined, dragster-inspired machine, the *Assault*, he broke the standing-start kilometre and mile records set by Bernd Rosemeyer in an Auto Union before World War II. The speeds were 132.94 mph and 149.93 mph respectively. By 1962 he had broken over 100 international, national or American records.

In 1961, Thompson had a major setback. He considered the possibility of attempting to beat the world water-speed record, but broke his back in a testing accident. Although doctors said he would never walk again, by 1963 he had completely recovered. His off-the-track sidelines included selling high-performance equipment for road cars, organising hot rod and custom shows and building cars for drag racing. In 1962, still recovering from his accident, he thought he ought to try to construct a car to win America's most prestigious and famous motor race, the Indianapolis 500.

Known as the Harvey Aluminium Specials after their sponsors, the Thompson-built cars were ahead of their time. Up until then American-built Indy machines had been outdated, front-engined devices. Thompson decided to try sophistication and requested designer John Crosthwaite to adopt both European Grand Prix-type thinking plus his own ideas. The result was a low, rear-engined machine, its engine a Buick V8 modified to produce 330 bhp. Three cars were entered, but only the one driven by Dan Gurney qualified for the race. After running in the front half of the field, Gurney retired with transmission failure on the 94th of the 200 laps.

For the 1963 race new cars, one-third lighter than conventional Indy machines, were built. Again low, but very wide and with clean lines, the cars used modified Chevrolet V8 engines and—pioneering later Grand Prix trends —featured wide, low-profile tyres specially made by Firestone. Duane Carter retired his with a blown engine, while Al Miller in a modified '62 car with a Chevy engine finished ninth. Graham Hill unsuccessfully attempted to qualify a new model. Ford-engined cars, known as Mickey Thompson Sears Allstate Specials, ran in 1964. Dave MacDonald crashed with fatal consequences; Eddie Johnson's fuel pump failed after six laps. A completely new concept arrived for the 1965 race: a monocoque machine known as the Challenger Wheel Special with a front-mounted, highly modified Chevrolet V8 engine driving the front wheels. Driver Bob Mathouser blew it up during the qualification runs and failed to make the grid. Thompson originally nominated himself as driver, but owing to heart-strain he collapsed in the seat of a record-breaking machine in the autumn. He would never have passed the Indianapolis Motor Speedway's medical check.

Thompson ended his speed career by breaking records. In 1967 and 1968, driving both a Ford Mustang and a Chevrolet Camaro, he broke many international, national and American records. With the Mustang (sharing with Danny Ongais over the longer distances), he cracked 500 km, 500-mile, 1000 km, 1000-mile, 5000 km, 1-hour, 6-hour, 12-hour and 14-hour records.   MK

Above: Mickey Thompson in his pick-up on one of the famous Baja races

Below: Mickey Thompson stands next to his amazing 27.2-litre quad-engined *Challenger I*

OUSTED BY THE COMMERCIAL

Thornycroft cars were eventually forced to give way to the more popular commercial vehicles produced by the company

Above: a 1911 18 hp 3726 cc car; this model was the company's last to be put into production, for commercial-vehicle manufacture was increased soon after

Top right: a 1904 two-seater

Right: another 1904 car, this vehicle is seen at Brighton on a recent London–Brighton veteran-car rally; Lord Brabazon of Tara is at the wheel

EVEN BEFORE JOHN I THORNEYCROFT founded his famous steam-launch company on the Thames at Chiswick in 1864, he had experimented with a steam road vehicle, but had abandoned this because of the restrictive laws of the period.

In 1895/6 he constructed one of the very earliest British commercial vehicles, a van powered by a compound steam-launch engine which drove the front wheels by chains; steering was obtained by a swivelling rear-axle, the steering handle taking 32 turns from lock to lock. The van weighed 30 cwt and could carry a load of one ton; still in running order, it is preserved today in the National Motor Museum. Four and six-wheeled Thorneycroft steam wagons took part in the Liverpool Trials of the Self-Propelled Traffic Association in 1898, the four-wheeler winning the third prize of £50, while the six-wheeler had a two-wheel attachment which the company subsequently claimed made it the original articulated lorry. Improved versions of this design won gold medals in the 1899 and 1901 SPTA Trials.

Thornycroft was perhaps the earliest company to supply motorised vehicles for municipal use, having built a number of steam tipping wagons for the Chiswick Urban District Council in 1896 and for Westminster City Council in 1899—the latter vehicle was still in service in 1924.

In 1903 the company which now had a factory at Basingstoke in Hampshire, entered the private car market with two models, a 10 hp twin-cylinder of 1814 cc and a 20 hp four-cylinder of 3628 cc. The cars were of up-to-date design, with channel steel chassis and live axle drive; one peculiarity was the use of V-shaped grooves in the external contracting brake drums, into which fitted the similarly contoured brake bands, with the idea of obtaining more positive contact between the friction surfaces.

The larger model had a further distinctive feature in the shape of a belt-driven dynamo, a fitting which would not become common on most vehicles for at least another decade. The 1905 range was of more modern appearance, and by 1906 the company could claim royal patronage, for they had supplied two 30 hp cars to the Princess Christian. There was also a 36 hp model.

The marque was not renowed for its sporting performances, though entries were made in the Isle of Man Tourist Trophy Races of 1905/8 and in the IoM Four Inch Race of 1908.

The year 1907 saw a range of new models—an 18 hp four-cylinder, a 30 hp four-cylinder and a 45 hp six-cylinder. This range continued unaltered into 1908, in which year *The Sphere* commented on the firm's showing at Olympia; 'The Thornycroft firm shows one of the finest six-cylinder chassis in the building and is justly proud of it. At a chassis price of £750 this really fine production is not to be beaten, while for simplicity and openness of design it is to be commended almost above any other exhibit of the kind. Rarely has there been a six-cylinder less cumbered with piping or one in which the valves and magneto are so acceptable. In the cheaper models, especially the 30 hp, Thornycrofts put a car on the market which should just suit the average driver who desires a just measure of power but has no taste for reckless speed.'

The 1911 range consisted of two models only, the 18 hp of 3726 cc and the 30 hp of 5185 cc; by 1912 only the 18 hp was being produced and in 1913, car production ceased altogether.   DBW

An early Finnish flier

FINLAND IS RENOWNED for its rally drivers. One of the most famous was Pauli Toivonen, once European Rally Champion and a winner of many famous 'classics'. Much of his early success was gained at the wheel of the Citroëns. After a season of misfortune with Lancia in 1967 he rallied Porsches to a succession of victories and once again put his name at the top.

Pauli Toivonen was born in Helsinki on 22 August 1929. As a youth he excelled at athletics and enjoyed playing in dance bands. Subsequently he became a car salesman in the town of Jyväskylä, well-known as the base of Finland's *Jyväskylän Suurajot*—or Rally of the 1000 Lakes. In 1954 Toivonen decided to begin rallying, thinking that if he made a name for himself he could sell a few more cars. With a Volkswagen 1200, he was 10th overall in the Rally of the 1000 Lakes, also winning his class, much to his astonishment.

Driving a selection of cars in Finnish rallies, Toivonen gradually built up a reputation—and sold more cars. In 1959, driving a Saab, he finished second in the Finnish Championship and purchased a Simca. Later he rallied a works-prepared Citroën ID19, venturing outside Scandinavia for the first time. On scratch, he was fourth in the 1961 Monte Carlo Rally, but because of the peculiar handicapping system was ultimately placed 41st. He was later second in the Rally of the 1000 Lakes, thus assuring himself of the Finnish Championship.

In 1962, now driving a full works Citroën, Toivonen had an accident in the Monte Carlo Rally, but he won the Rally of the 1000 Lakes, was third in the Finnish Hankirallyt, won the Viking and Winter rallies in Norway, was a class winner in the Swedish Rally. He became Scandinavian Champion.

For the following year Toivonen achieved second place for Citroën in the Monte Carlo Rally, seventh in the Acropolis and a win the in the Hankirallyt. A move to Volkswagen was made for 1964, but it was an unsuccessful year. Tenth overall (and a class win) in the Monte Carlo Rally with a 1500S was about his best showing. In 1965, a year in which he also rallied a Porsche 904 GTS, the Finn was third in the Rally of the 1000 Lakes behind the works Mini-Cooper Ss of Timo Mäkinen and Rauno Aaltonen. He was driving a Volkswagen 1500S.

In 1966, driving a Citroën DS21, Toivonen was declared winner of the Monte Carlo Rally. But it was a hollow victory. British works Mini-Cooper Ss, provisionally placed first, second and third, plus a Ford Cortina Lotus which was fourth, were all excluded for alleged lighting infringements. Later in the year he rallied a Renault and in 1967 he joined Lancia, taking sixth place in the Swedish Rally and seventh in the Rally of the 1000 Lakes in a Fulvia HF model. Mechanical problems caused him to retire from the Monte Carlo and Acropolis rallies.

By now Toivonen appeared to be overshadowed by fellow-countrymen Mäkinen and Aaltonen. But that was to change in 1968. This was Toivonen's greatest year, the 38-year-old Finn signed to drive a works Porsche 911T in European Rally Championship events. He began the year with a close second to team-mate Vic Elford in the Monte Carlo Rally, then he won the San Remo Rally, the East German Rally and

Above: Pauli Toivonen at the wheel of his Lancia Fulvia HF on the 1967 Monte Carlo rally; the Lancia later retired in the event. After a fairly lean season with the Italian concern, Pauli switched allegiance to Porsche of Germany

West Germany's Wiesbaden Rally. After a third place in the Acropolis Rally (he would have been better placed, but the car fell off a broken jack), he won the Donau Rally, the Spanish Rally and—a mere four days after its finish—the Geneva Rally. Toivonen was undisputed European Rally Champion. His one regret, however, was that he crashed in his 'home' event, the Rally of the 1000 Lakes.

The 1969 season was Toivonen's last in competitive rallying, co-inciding with Porsche's cutback in their rally programme. He crashed in the Monte Carlo Rally, but made amends by winning the Acropolis. Toivonen was also seen in circuit racing for Porsche. In the Targa Florio he shared a Porsche 911R with Dieter Spoerry, but retired in the third lap when it caught fire, while in an out-and-out racing Porsche 908/02 he retired in the Circuit of Mugello through driver fatigue—clutch trouble in practice meant his intended co-driver Gérard Larrouse did not qualify, so Toivonen was forced to race single-handed. He led the first lap, but then dropped back and was forced to retire owing to the heat.

Following his retirement from the sport, Toivonen became a sales director for the Porsche and Chrysler agents in Finland.   MK

An Ace up his sleeve

AS A MECHANICALLY MINDED but sport-starved Europe emerged from the toils of the Hitler war, the motoring enthusiasts of the most car-conscious countries developed their own nationally characteristic sports cars. The Italians sought to bring out the sporting flavour in their Fiat 1100s, which was easy; the Germans tried to improve upon the BMW 328, which was difficult; and the French attempted to give the front-drive Citroën and the rear-engined Renault some semblance of high-performance respectability, which was practically impossible. In Britain, thanks to the absence of any enemy occupying forces and the presence of the Vintage Sports Car Club, there was a good supply of impressive cars with a certain elegance born in a happier age, and certain massiveness bred on the bumps of Brooklands; but those whom neither sentiment nor taste moved to join this society of high-velocity antiquarians turned to the little 1.25-litre MG, which was one of the first sporting cars to go into production in Britain as the car factories resumed their peacetime role. The MG TC undoubtedly put the British sports car on the American map, but to the competition-minded driver at home that was an irrelevance: its bodywork could be criticised for its excesses, and its chassis execrated for its shortcomings, but its engine was capable of being tuned to give respectable power, its gearbox could be tolerated despite the wide ratios prompted by a trials background, and it was available. An assortment of little Specials based to a greater or less extent on the TC soon flourished.

Prominent among these was the Lester MG, built at a little workshop in Hertfordshire by Harry Lester. Its chassis was a simple ladder-like structure of two fairly large diameter tubes, braced transversely at convenient points, and graced with independent front suspension of wishbone type. The MG engine was often linered down to bring it within the 1100 cc class or enlarged to approach the next limit of 1500 cc, and was tuned by conventional means to give the very light car, with its slim slipper-type body and sketchy cycle wings, a surprisingly lively performance which brought a number of successes in some of the better-publicised club events of the time.

These results encouraged John Tojeiro to develop the Lester chassis further. His first efforts were also made in Hertfordshire, at Royston. In 1950 he determined to try his hand at building a run of cars which was to number 50 before he finished. As well as using MG engines, he produced versions powered by the more substantial and potentially very powerful Lea-Francis, and also by the lightweight air-cooled V-twin JAP.

The Tojeiro-Jap was a tiny car and weighed very little. Its engine was set well forward (just behind the front suspension) with its crank-shaft longitudinal, and its two cylinders poking out through holes in the shallow bonnet, giving it a faintly comical appearance; but the rabid engine

gave the car a ferocity that quite belied its looks, and it was in this model that Archie Scott-Brown, after a brief novitiate behind an MG engine, began to make his indelible, but lamentably brief, mark on the motor-racing scene.

The notoriety of the Tojeiro JAP was nothing compared with the fame of the Tojeiro Bristol that the little Hertfordshire factory built next. Once again the chassis was a simple twin-tube ladder, now with independent suspension of front and rear wheels by a combination of lower wishbones and upper transverse leaf springs, modelled on the fashion set by Cooper. The Bristol engine and gearbox promised a much higher level of performance than anything Tojeiro had built previously, and in another stroke of inspired conceptul larceny, Tojeiro gave the car an open two-seater body styled somewhat approximately after the fashion of the Barchetta body of the Ferrari 166 MM. It was not quite as beautifully porportioned as the Ferrari, for the Bristol engine was uncomfortably tall, nor did the body-building skills available in Hertfordshire extend to producing the horizontal ridges that relieved the flanks of the Ferrari and made it look so graceful. Nevertheless it was an effective, practical, smooth body that was blessedly light and as reasonably free from drag-raisers as anything about at the time. The car was in fact phenomenally successful in the hands of Cliff Davis, who made its registration number LOY 500 famous within a few months as he raced from success to success around the British circuits. JOY 500 was equally well known, and soon it was clear that John Tojeiro had hit upon a very effective formula for the creation of a competitive two-seater.

He was therefore emboldened to offer the design to AC of Thames Ditton, whose own cars were beginning to falter in their appeal to sporting drivers, handicapped as they were by outsize chassis and bodies that were far too burdensome for the age-old AC two-litre engine. Thus it came about that, at the 1953 Earls Court Show, AC exhibited a new and stimulating Ace, essentially the Tojeiro design, but with the old faithful AC engine taking the place of the Bristol. What with the reduction in power to a mere 85 bhp, and the increase in weight inevitably associated with the trimmings and trappings of a road-going production car, the Ace could not hope to rival the scintillating performance of the Tojeiro Bristol in a straight line. Around corners it suffered somewhat from the limitations of its engine yet again, for centrifugal force created problems of oil surge that could make the car run out of bearings before it ran out of road. Soon the engine was improved at top and bottom, until it developed

Right: one of a famous pair: *JOY 500* the 1952 Cooper-MG, designed and built by John Tojeiro and campaigned successfully by Cliff Davis

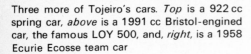

Three more of Tojeiro's cars. *Top* is a 922 cc spring car, *above* is a 1991 cc Bristol-engined car, the famous LOY 500, and, *right*, is a 1958 Ecurie Ecosse team car

105 bhp and could even maintain most of that going around corners—something that the Ace did very well by the standards of the time, calling forth unstinted praise for its handling in the pages of contemporary motoring journals.

Whatever its shortcomings—and it did have some, including rather unsatisfactory steering gear, and a certain susceptibility to vapour lock in the fuel system (discovered the hard way in the Alpine Trial), the Ace was very well received, and as it was gradually improved it earned more and more respect, tempered only by a little regret at limitations of the old engine. Within a couple of years AC had persuaded Bristol to make them a cheap quantity-produced version of their BS sports engine, the 100 D2, which was installed in the Ace chassis with an output of 128 bhp. It was a less flexible engine than the AC but much more powerful, and if it was not as light its gearbox was lighter, as well as being blessed with ratios and an action much more appropriate to its duties. The result was that the Ace Bristol was one of the most formidable sports cars in Britain, and in its subsequent development the Ace did great things for the Thames Ditton firm. Indeed, had AC not succumbed to the temptation to get mixed up with Carrol Shelby and American Ford V8 engines, they might have continued to prosper for longer than they did—but on the other hand we would have been denied the thrill of the AC

Cobra, which was a sort of Tojeiro taken to the point of absurdity.

Tojeiro himself, having sold his twin-tube designs to AC, went a stage further with a multi-tubular chassis that recognised some of the principles of the spaceframe. Into this, a 1955 development, he contrived to fit a variety of engines ranging in size up to the D-type Jaguar version which gave Jack Brabham 250 bhp to play with in 1957. Despite the advantages of so much power and the De Dion rear suspension, this type was never very successful, though not for the want of trying on the part of Ecurie Ecosse. Rather better results were obtained with a 1958 version carrying an 1100 cc Coventry Climax engine and sporting a single disc transmission brake.

Tojeiro was not slow to appreciate the virtues of the rear-engined layout that so rapidly turned the tables on the Grand Prix scene, and by 1960 was building racing cars for lesser events, notably Formula Junior, with the engine behind the driver. Inevitably they looked like the current Coopers, just as the original Tojeiro Bristol did when shorn of its bodywork—and since 1960 was the year when the Cooper factory demonstrated that it had done all it could, the resemblance was perhaps unfortunate and ill-judged. At any rate the rear engined Tojeiros were not successful.

They fared no better when they were labelled

as Britannias. The little firm of Britannia Cars Limited, another Hertfordshire tiddler, had been set up in 1957 to build yet another of the variously inspired and insipid contraptions that poured from the resin-reeking backyards of Britain in the 1950s and early 1960s. This one had a fairly ambitious specification, with disc brakes and independent suspension for all wheels, and a Ford Zephyr engine within the usual glassfibre-reinforced plastics GT body. Tojeiro had had some say in its design, but presumably none in its manufacture or marketing, until the firm failed, whereupon he took it over. Beneath its banner he sold some Formular Junior cars overseas, and created an attractively developed version of the GT car with a Chevrolet Corvette engine replacing the Ford. The venture was not attended by any business success, and once again he turned to racing prototypes, building rear-engined cars with Buick, Jaguar, and Coventry Climax engines. He still found some support among the drivers of Ecurie Ecosse, who entered a Climax Tojeiro for the race at Le Mans; but the car was troublesome mechanically and somewhat incontinent in its handling. Before long both Britannia and Tojeiro were out of production. The AC Ace and its pretty closed version, the Aceca, survived rather longer, and the original Tojeiro Bristol is unlikely to be forgotten by those who saw it in action in its heyday.   LJKS

ALL PART OF THE SERVICE

Every workshop should contain a number of basic tools necessary for the car owner to maintain his vehicle

THERE ARE CERTAIN TOOLS—they can be called the basics—that no workshop can do without. These basics have many adaptations and developments, which are usually great time and effort savers. Then, listed under miscellaneous, are more specialised tools, which are essential for some jobs, but would not normally be obtained until specifically required. In addition, there are a number of special tools, needed for certain jobs on particular makes of car. Often, it is more economical to hire these—and some of the more specialised and expensive tools, such as torque wrenches—which are only required occasionally. Although not strictly a tool in the accepted sense, a substantial workbench is a first requirement of any workshop.

One great enemy of tools is rust—fine tools, such as feeler gauges, engineers' squares, scribers and the like, should always have a little thin oil applied after use. Heavier tools are not so affected, although a box of rusty spanners reflects no credit on its owner.

Choose the tool to suit the job—light tools used for heavy work can be easily strained or bent and become unsafe or unless. If in doubt, seek instruction as to the correct way to use a tool—you will be well repaid by longer tool life and better results. Be careful always to collect up all tools after working on a car engine—a spanner falling into the fan blades when the engine is started can have embarrassing, if not dangerous, results.

Before any job is started, the various parts will almost certainly need to be cleaned. For removing accumulated dirt from unpainted surfaces, make a start with the wire brush, followed by paraffin (kerosene)-soaked rags. Small parts can be soaked clean in a paraffin-filled tray. Tar and oil on paintwork can be removed by trichlorethylene or a proprietary cleaner. Always spread a lint-free cloth over the bench before dismantling an assembly, or before working on delicate parts.

The simple 'one-leg' jack supplied by the car manufacturer will lift one or two wheels, but never work beneath the car in this condition—always add supports, such as substantial wooden billets or proper axle stands, and lower the vehicle onto these; do not use

Left: the back of a van, specially equipped with tools, used to follow the course of a rally and look after the troubles of a particular car or team of cars

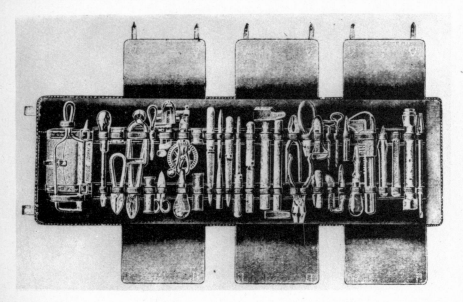

refers to the head. Hammers usually have one flat head and either a ball pein (for riveting) or a straight or cross pein. The short-handled, double-faced club hammer is an ideal portable back support block. There are many additional types of hammer used in panel beating. To avoid damage to knock-on wheel nuts, for example, which require some force to release them, a hide-lead-faced hammer should be used; for lighter work, copper, nylon, all hide or rubber-faced mallets are available. Always keep hammer heads tight—using metal wedges—and replace split or damaged handles. If a hammer head is chipped or cracked, replace it at once.

For easily accessible hexagon nuts and bolt heads, regular or the thinner spearhead open-ended spanners are used; there is also a slim series of spearhead spanners, for use with the narrower locknuts. A variation is the obstruction spanner, which has its jaws open towards the side, instead of the end, of the spanner. The ring and the offset ring spanners are useful for awkward locations, and there are many combinations of ring and open-ended spanner, both straight and cranked. For spark plugs and for nuts

Above: in the early days of motoring, the tool kit provided with a car was far more comprehensive than in later years; it included a number of carpenter's tools, which were necessary in order to carry out maintenance on the body and wheels

Right: the type of wheel-nut wrench commonly known as a 'spider' and used by many professional mechanics for various sizes of wheel nut

Far right: a selection of spanners, all very useful in the modern motor car; the open-ended and ring types can be used on most nuts, but the adjustable variety is useful for odd sizes, while the box is handy for inaccessible nuts and bolts

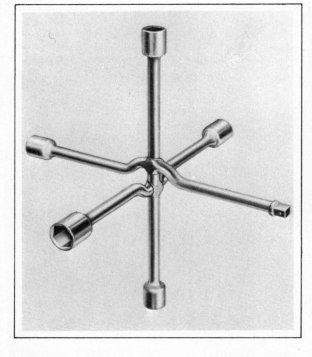

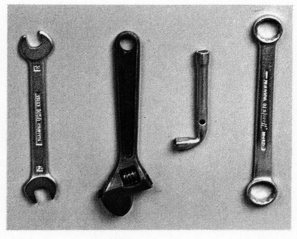

where side space is very limited, the tubular box spanner, operated a 'tommy bar' through holes in the spanner, is an essential. Box spanners are normally double-ended and available in two lengths and two grades—grade *A* is the better quality, made from heat-treated steel. Torque wrenches enable a nut to be tightened down to a specified torque, which is read off a scale set in the handle; some models can be set to slip if a pre-set torque is exceeded. Various torque ranges are available. Adjustable-jaw spanners are available in variety; they save time but are prone to stretch and ultimately slip in use. Socket spanners, with square snap-on drives and operated by a cranked bar, ratchet, brace or torque bar, can be obtained in boxed sets and they save a lot of space.

The nominal sizes of all these spanners for Whitworth and BS bolts and nuts are based on the bolt diameter, but as these thread types have the same size nut and bolt head for different bolt diameters, the spanners have dual markings, eg, $\frac{1}{4}$ BS $\frac{3}{16}$ W; $\frac{5}{8}$ BS $\frac{9}{16}$ W. BA sizes are marked with their BA number, while Unified and metric nominal sizes are marked on their widths across flats (AF)—the width between opposite faces—in hundredths of an inch or millimetres, respectively.

For gripping pipes and round fittings where some surface burring is not of consequence, the adjustable pipe wrench of the Stillson type is invaluable. The nominal size is the overall length of the tool in inches when the jaws are fully open. For gripping larger

bricks as supports: they can crumble. Always block wheels resting on the ground, both before and behind.

Screwdrivers range in size from the tiny jewellers, for delicate instrument work, to the 11 in (300 mm) blade, heavy-duty type. With these large sizes, a square blade is sometimes fitted to enable turning assistance to be given by a spanner. Keep the end of the blade ground square so that it will fit snugly into the slot; screwdrivers always wear to a chisel edge eventually and in this condition may slip and cause damage when pressure is applied. The ratchet screwdriver is a very useful time-saving tool. Many automobile fixings today use cross or star-headed screws, requiring a *Phillips* or *Posidrive* screwdriver.

The hand lamp, with earthed guard, saves fumbling around in the dark—a fluorescent lamp operated from the battery is a useful development.

Hammers are available in a range of weights, from the 4 oz (100 g) pin (or telephone) hammer to the 3-pounder (1.3 kg) for really heavy blows: the weight

diameters, especially where surface marking is not acceptable, such as on hub or radiator caps, lamp flanges, etc, the rope grip or strap spanner is used. The basis of these devices is a length of flexible material that can be wrapped around the object and gripped by a handle which acts as a lever.

Allen Keys are hexagonal bars bent to give a short operating end and a longer handle. Their function is to turn socket-head screws; wheel braces are for wheel nuts which provide good leverage and usually 4 or 6 different sizes in one tool; drain-plug spanners, multiple-ended or adjustable, will fit a wide range of male and female sump, gear-box and rear-axle filler and drain plugs; adjustable hook or 'C' spanners are used for slotted-edge ring nuts. Special brake-adjusting spanner sets are available to suit various types of drum and disc brakes.

An electric light-weight 65 watt pencil-bit type, using flux-cored solder, is suitable for electric wiring; but for sheet metal work, copper bits from 2 oz (57 g) to 32 oz (908 g) are available. These solid bits can conveniently be heated by bottled gas. Baker's Fluid is an excellent flux for this type of work. When soldering, freshly clean both surfaces, apply flux liberally, heat the metal being soldered and apply the solder to the metal, not to the soldering iron; if Baker's Fluid or other acid flux is used, wash it off.

Centre punches are ground to a point, to enable a small hole to be impressed on a metal surface for guiding a drill or as a datum point from which measurements can be taken. The automatic centre punch is a great time-saver; it is a spring-loaded device in which hand pressure is sufficient to compress an internal spring. At an adjustable set point, the spring is triggered and drives the punch into the metal.

Motor punches have a flat-ended, gently tapered shank and are designed to knock out taper pins; parallel-pin and inserted-pin punches are flat-ended with parallel shanks of various diameters and are used for knocking out keys, cotter pins and the like.

Engineers' chisels are used for marking and cutting metal, for chopping off rusty bolts and similar work. They can be resharpened with a file.

The vice (vise) is an essential bench-mounted tool for holding parts that require sawing, drilling, bending or filing. The 'quick-grip' type saves time and is obtainable with various jaw sizes. Fibre liners can be slipped over the jaws to hold threaded or small-diameter pieces firmly and without damage. Always keep the movable jaw screw and bearings well greased. The engineers' clamp, the 'C' clamp and the hand vice are portable tools used to hold two parts together temporarily.

For larger round sections, the vee block and clamp holds round bars or pipes up to $1\frac{1}{2}$ in (40 mm) diameter securely for drilling or other operations.

Tinman's shears (Tinsnips) are for cutting sheet metal along a previously scribed line. Obtain the open-ended variety, otherwise the ends of the handles can inflict a nasty nip. Cranked snips, easier to operate on heavier-gauge metals, are also available.

There is no more useful—or misused—tool than a pair of pliers. They will legitimately grip, pull, turn, twist and cut; they are wrongly used as spanners (thus ruining the nuts) and hammers (thus ruining the pliers). Besides the insulated-handle combination pliers, which incorporate a wirecutter in their pivoted centre, there are slip-joint pliers to cover a wider range of openings, channel-lock pliers to cover an even wider range; parrot-jaw pliers to grip behind an obstruction; mole grip (vise grip) pliers, which can be attached firmly to an object, leaving both hands free, and taper or snipe pliers for manipulating small components and bending wires. For wiring jobs, side or end cutters or the combined cutter-stripper (to remove the insulation without damaging the wire) are used. Circlip pliers, in various sizes, can be obtained for handling circlips.

The hacksaw is universally used for cutting metal of all kinds. Hacksaw blades are graded in teeth per inch (tpi). Use a

14 tpi blade for soft materials over 13 mm thick
18 tpi blade for soft materials 6 to 13 mm thick
24 tpi blade for soft materials 3 to 6 mm thick and hard materials 3 to 13 mm thick and a 32 tpi blade for all tubes and for all materials under 3 mm thick.

A miniature 6 in (150 mm)-blade hacksaw is ideal for fine work. Always insert the blade with the points away from the handle, and tighten it as much as possible before commencing to saw. Keep the blade straight while sawing, otherwise it may snap into pieces.

The *Stanley* knife, with heavy-duty blade, is intended for cutting or trimming gaskets, leather or other soft material.

Above: a comprehensive socket set from the famous King Dick company; sockets are the most reliable and easiest spanners to use provided that access to the nut is available over the end of the bolt

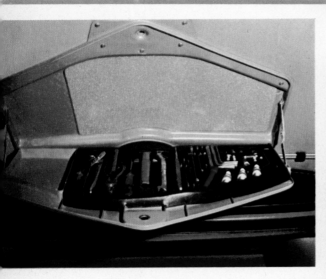

A selection of sharp files should be in every tool kit. Their purpose is to smooth out irregularities after sawing as well as to shape and enlarge holes and similar work. Files are manufactured in many shapes, usually 9 or 12 in (230 or 300 mm) long. The more common shapes are: hand (parallel sides); flat (tapered sides); round; half-round; half-oval; square; triangular; single and double-ended. They come in 5 cuts: rough; smooth; bastard; single; second.

Hand files can be obtained with a 'safe edge'—which has no serrations, so that the flat surface can be used on one side of a square while the safe edge protects the adjacent side. When filing, always hold the workpiece firmly in a vice, if possible, and maintain the file level—lighten the pressure on the toe of the file at the start of the stroke and on the heel of the file towards the end of the stroke.

A wooden file handle can be fitted to the tang of a file; this protects the hand and facilitates grip. Use your newest file on the hardest material; an old file will still cut brass or aluminium. When the file is clogged, do not clean it with a wire brush or so-called 'filed cording'—nothing will blunt it so quickly—but use a stiff nylon brush. A range of needle files, approximately 6 in (150 mm) long, in a greater variety of shapes, is obtainable for fine work. A sharp file tang is a most useful tool for the rough enlargement of a hole in sheet metal.

The oil can, which should be filled with clean engine oil, eases many a squeaky hinge and catch.

Straight-shank drills are required for the wheel brace (or hand brace) and electric drill, and are available in $\frac{1}{64}$ in steps, from $\frac{1}{16}$ in up to $\frac{1}{2}$ in, or in $\frac{1}{2}$ mm steps from 1 mm up to 13 mm.

Good quality 'high-speed' or 'high-tensile' steel drills should always be chosen in preference to the 'carbon-steel' variety, which are relatively soft and break easily. Unless engineering on a large scale is contemplated, it is preferable to buy a number of the commonly used sizes, so that a sharp drill of the wanted size is always available, rather than a wide-ranging graduated set of drills, however impressive a large drill stand may look. Drills must be kept sharp; if an electric grinder is not available, a toolmakers' services should be sought. A countersinking bit is a valuable addition to the drill box.

The feeler gauge consists of a number of parallel or taper blades, accurately ground to the thickness etched on each blade; both Imperial and metric sizes are available. Sets with between 8 and 26 blades can be obtained, ranging in thickness from 0.0015 to 0.025 in, or 0.3 to 1.00 mm. Wipe the blades clean before use; if

a blade of the correct thickness is not available, two or more blades may be paired up. When measuring clearances, remember that, if one part is worn to a cavity and the mating part fits into that cavity, the feeler gauge will not give a true reading as it will bridge across the cavity; the parts must be ground true for accurate measurement.

The steel rule is an essential for marking out and general measurements. Rules are available from 4 in (100 mm) to 3 ft (1 metre) in length, usually engraved with both English and metric scales. Rules with the new rustless chrome face have proved a great boon to legibility.

Here are a selection of specialised tools, and their purposes, that may come in handy.

For sharpening drills and chisels—the electric grinder. When operating this grinder, wear goggles; for examining under surfaces—a hand mirror; for locating that elusive engine knock—the stethoscope; for handling valve springs—a valve-spring compressor; for greasing nipples—the grease gun; for removing rusting nuts, when all else has failed—the hydraulic nut-splitter; for removing snapped-off studs or bolts—the screw extractor; for more permanent (and safer) lifting—a pair of ramps, the wheeled garage jack and axle stands; for removing road wheels, half-shafts, steering wheels, king pins, ball races or gears—a variety of pullers and extractors; for checking and identifying screw threads—the screw-pitch-recognition gauge; for replacing pistons, with rings, into the cylinder—the piston-ring clamp or compressor; for opening out holes accurately—the reamer or the expanding reamer; for valve grinding—a suction valve grinder, to grip the valve, and coarse and fine valve-grinding paste; for a weak battery—a battery charger; for cutting screw threads—taps for holes and dies for rods, requiring a tap wrench and a die holder, respectively, to manipulate them; for accurate measuring of thicknesses, diameters, bored holes—the external and the internal micrometer; for masking out, prior to cutting or drilling—marking-out blue, the engineer's square, the adjustable bevel, the centre square, the scriber, dividers; for testing the fit of bearings, and clearances—engineer's blue; for transferring measurements—inside and outside calipers and for removing door handles—the door-handle spring clip or pin remover. AGH

TAKING A TURN FOR THE BETTER

Torque is a subject that causes much controversy among motor enthusiasts as it is very difficult to define this confusing term exactly

Above: drag racers produce an enormous amount of torque— enough indeed to lift the front wheels and driver far off the ground

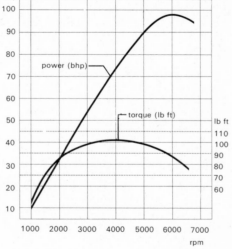

In theory, the torque produced by an internal-combustion engine should be a constant amount, independent of engine speed; in practice, mechanical inefficiencies limit the mean engine pressure, and thus the torque, at low and high engine speeds. Power rises with speed, but once again inefficiency causes a fall off at high speed

TORQUE IS THE POWER of a twisting or rotating force; it is the product of one of two equal, opposite and parallel offset forces and the distance between them. Applied to the motor car, this means the effort exerted on a shaft to move the vehicle along; when torque is great enough to move the shaft through a given distance in a given time, then this is expressed as power and is measured in horsepower. It follows from this that the difference between torque and power is that power involves movement whereas torque does not (horsepower depends on the number of crankshaft revolutions which take place in a given time as a result of torque).

In theory, torque is independent of engine speed, the figure being totally dependent on the mean effective pressure in the cylinders (the mean effective pressure is calculated by subtracting the sum of the average pressures on the induction, compression and exhaust strokes from the average pressure on the expansion stroke). In practice, however, the mean effective pressure (mep) of the engine does decrease at high engine speeds and this reduces the torque. In practical applications mep is calculated from the brake horsepower figure for a particular engine, which means that it is an imaginary figure, taking into account the inefficiency of the engine; in this case, mep becomes brake mean effective pressure (bmep).

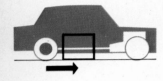

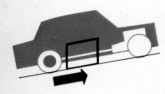

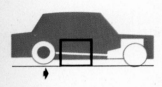

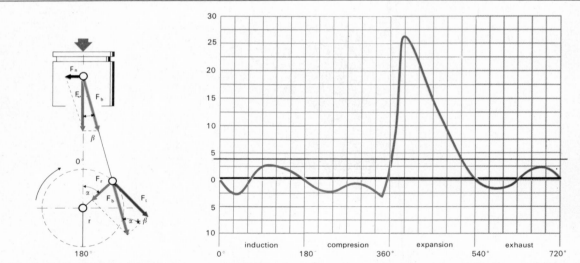

Torque and bmep are related as follows:

$$\text{torque (lb ft)} = \frac{\text{bmep(lb/in}^2) \times \text{swept volume (cc)}}{2473}$$

where 2473 represents a constant.

A further formula relates the torque figure to the power output of the engine at a particular speed.

$$\text{torque (lb ft)} = \frac{\text{bhp} \times 5250}{\text{rpm}}$$

where the figure 5250 is a constant which, among other things, equates the various units.

It can be seen from the second formula that if the torque remains constant the power output will rise with speed. This is theoretically absolute but practically less so: engine speed is limited by mechanical considerations, but, as we have already seen, the bmep decreases as speed rises, so the power output, too, will fall. The reason for the fall off in bmep and torque is not simply increased friction; as engine speed increases, so ideally should the size of the induction passages, in order to maintain something very close to atmospheric pressure in those tubes. As the pressure here falls, so the cylinders receive a smaller charge of fuel and air on the induction stroke, and so the expansion pressure falls.

Compression ratio is very important in determining the bmep and the torque output of an engine: the higher the compression ratio the higher these figures

Above: if a metal bar of low torsional rigidity were to be inserted in the propeller shaft of a car, it would demonstrate the torque being applied to the wheels; the torque required to climb a hill (centre) is greater than that needed for a level road (top), while if the rear wheels are lifted off the road surface they will spin freely, with very little torque involved (Bottom)

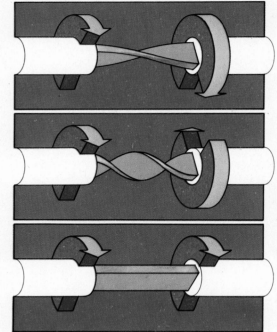

The force F, acting on the piston, is composed of the force F_b, acting on the con-rod, and the force F_n which provokes a lateral thrust on the cylinder wall. The driving torque is represented by the product of the force F_b and its minimum distance from its axis, which is the product of $F_t(F_b \times \sin[\alpha + \beta])$ and the radius of the crankshaft r. The graph show the variation of torque as a function of crankshaft angle (α); the mauve line represents the average torque for the four strokes.

This diagram demonstrates the effect of torque on a metal bar; the amount by which the bar twists is directly proportional to the torque applied to the lever, which in turn depends on the length of the bar and the force applied to it

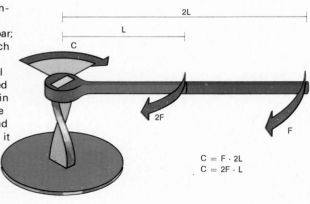

$$C = F \cdot 2L$$
$$C = 2F \cdot L$$

become. Unfortunately, however, there is a practical limit, in that knock begins to occur at high compression ratios and, although this can be delayed, it is ultimately unavoidable.

Torque is a word which is used in other ways as far as the car is concerned. The most important nuts and bolts used to fix the components together are tightened to a predetermined torque. So as to achieve these settings, a torque spanner, or torque wrench, is used. In its simplest form, this comprises a spring-steel bar attached to a square socket-spanner drive; also attached to this squared end is a pointer which remains stationary as the bar bends; the scale attached to it passes the pointer. The scale is usually calibrated in lb ft or in kg metres and this provides a good illustration of torque. If the bar is one foot long and a force of one pound is applied at one end, then the torque on the other end will be 1 lb ft.   IW

ONE OF RACING'S OLDEST

THE TOURIST TROPHY is the world's oldest surviving motor race. It is a year older than the Targa Florio and the very first Grand Prix, although from time to time there have been breaks of several years between races. The TT's format has often changed, starting with races for touring cars with an interlude for sports cars before in recent years reverting to touring machinery.

Over the years, the Royal Automobile Club's Tourist Trophy has changed much in format. In its time it has been Britain's premier motor race; on other occasions it has been but a mere shadow of its former self. It is a series steeped in history with an illustrious list of past winners including Rudi Caracciola and Tazio Nuvolari. Stirling Moss won it a record number of seven times.

At the turn of the century, when the British Government forbade racing on public roads there was nowhere for pioneer racing motorists to compete in Britain until Brooklands was opened in 1907. Well, not quite. Fortunately both the Isle of Man and Northern Ireland were able to pass their own laws and they allowed the closing of roads for racing.

The Automobile Club of Great Britain & Ireland announced details of the first Tourist Trophy early in 1905. It was to be run in September on the 52-mile Isle of Man circuit used for the previous year's Gordon Bennett eliminating trial. It started on the steep

Below: two Ferrari 250GTOs head the start of the 1963 Tourist Trophy race at Goodwood; car No. 11, driven by Graham Hill, went on to win the race

Alexandra Drive in the north-west suburbs of Douglas and the route climbed then descended south-westwards towards Castletown. Turning north, the circuit climbed and fell and turned north-westwards towards the coastal town of Peel. Up the coast road it went and then took an indirect route eastwards to Ramsey. The Ramsey to Douglas road which completed the course comprised a climb to the Bungalow at 1596 ft above sea level and a downhill run back to the start/finish area.

As befitted its name, the first Tourist Trophy was for touring cars, with a set of regulations governing such items as fuel consumption (22.54 mpg minimum), weight (between 1300 and 1600 lb), wheelbase (7 ft 6 in minimum), load (660 lb to be made up by the mechanic, passenger or sand ballast in 50 lb bags), bodywork (of touring type for a driver and three passengers) and production (duplicates must be available to interested parties at a fixed price for one month after the race). There were 42 starters (28 British, 14 foreign), of which 18 finished (16 British, two foreign) the four laps. A pre-race favourite, the Hon Charles Rolls, the 28-year-old adventurer, stripped the gearbox of his Rolls-Royce 20-hp model minutes from the start and in an eventful race John Napier's flat-twin-engined, 3.8-litre Arrol-Johnston triumphed by 2 m 9 s over the Rolls-Royce 18 hp of Percy Northey. Napier was also credited with fastest lap of 1 h 31 m 9 s, 34.30 mph.

Such was the popularity of the first Tourist Trophy it was decided to repeat the event in 1906. This time an abbreviated course of 40.25 miles was used to minimise disruption—it meant the closing of one instead of five level crossings—which cut out the journey south to Castletown and the western coastal road. Slight rule amendments were made: the minimum wheelbase length was stretched to 8 ft, the fuel consumption limit was now 25 mpg, while to ensure special gear ratios were not used cars had to cover half-a-mile at 12 mph in top gear and make a standing start on a 1-in-6 gradient in bottom gear before the race. This time Rolls was an easy winner in a more powerful Rolls-Royce 22 hp model, winning by 25 m 57.6 s and setting best lap of 1 h 0 m 13.6 s, 39.90 mph. A. E. George (Argyll) would have finished second, but his car was disqualified for being underweight. It transpired that the car's floor-boards were not strong enough to take the strain of the 50 lb sandbags which splintered the boards and fell on to the circuit along with such items as the tools, the contents of the tonneau and finally the boards themselves! This gave the position to France's Paul Bablot in a 3.8-litre Berliet. Unfortunately, several of the competitors ran out of their fuel allocation on the last lap.

The organisers—now known as the Royal Automobile Club—decided to run two races simultaneously in 1907. The Tourist Trophy itself was extended to six laps, while the concurrent Heavy Tourist race was designed to attract larger machinery. But the race, run in fearfully wet conditions, was a farce. If the elements didn't claim the cars, the fuel consumption limits did, and there were only two finishers in each category (the Heavies eventually only had to cover five laps because of the conditions). Winner of the TT was E. Courtis in

2337

his 3.5-litre Rover 20 hp, while G. P. Mills (Beeston-Humber) was best of the Heavies.

Obviously a new format had to be found, but there was an outcry—led by *The Times*—when the RAC unveiled their 'Four Inch' proposals for 1908. In effect, the trend went away from touring machinery. The minimum weight limit was 1600 lb, engines were to have a maximum of four cylinders, each having a maximum bore of 4 in. There was no fuel consumption limit. In defence to adverse press criticism, the RAC decided to reduce the course to 37.75 miles on safety grounds and other safety precautions taken, such as the filling in of ditches, the removal of a ruined cottage which blocked drivers' vision and advance warning of each corner. A. E. George appeared to have the race sewn up, driving his 5-litre Darracq superbly as others crashed around the tough circuit—though not with the bloody results the multitude of press men anticipated. On the last lap a carburettor fire lost George his victory and he had to be satisfied with third behind W. Watson's Napier-Hutton and Algy Lee Guinness' Darracq.

The TT was revived in 1914, being open to cars up to 3310 cc and a minimum weight of 2300 lb. The race was run in two eight-lap parts over two days and there were

to Northern Ireland, to the 13.6-mile Ards circuit east of Belfast. Like many old true road circuits, it was the 'classic triangle' joining the towns of Dundonald, Newtownards and Comber. It possessed a variety of hazards and provided a challenge to any racing driver. Harry Ferguson was the instigator of reviving the TT

Right: Louis Gérard in his 3-litre Delage on his way to victory in the 1938 TT at Donington

E. SWAIN.

Right: the 1922 TT was held at the Isle of Man; here, we see a three-litre Vauxhall scampering round a dusty corner. Two of the three-car Vauxhall team, including this one, retired

cash prizes to add to the Trophy, the *Daily Telegraph* offering £1000 to the winner. Amid much publicity—not damning this time—the race attracted a large crowd. The 3.3-litre Sunbeams of Kenelm and Algy Lee Guinness dominated the race, but on the second day Algy's retired owing to a seized universal joint, leaving victory to brother Kenelm. Only six of the 22 starters survived. Nine cars entered the first post-World War I TT, held in 1922, when a 3-litre limit applied, so the RAC ran a simultaneous event for 1500 cc machines. Jean Chassagne's Sunbeam won, comfortably beating the enthusiastically driven Bentley of Frank Clement. Sir Algernon Lee Guiness' Talbot-Darracq gained the 1500 Trophy, run over six laps instead of the eight of the TT machinery.

Between 1928 and 1936 the Tourist Trophy moved

in Northern Ireland, although his original intention of emulating the Le Mans organisers by running a 24-hour sports-car race was vetoed by the Government.

Regulations for the 1928 TT reverted almost to touring regulations. The race was open to production sports cars and a handicapping system devised to that, in theory, J. D. Barnes' 747 cc Austin 7 had the same chance as T. Thistlethwayte's 6788 cc supercharged Mercedes-Benz 36/220s (in fact, the Mercedes and Bentley works teams withdrew as they thought the odds were against them). Eighty-eight pairs of legs sprinted for the Le Mans-type start, some drivers being so eager to get away they almost left their riding mechanics behind! Kaye Don's 1½-litre Lea-Francis conquered Leon Cushman's 1½-litre front-wheel-drive Alvis by a scant 13 s after almost six hours of exacting racing.

Top: the 1929 TT at Ulster sees the Alfa Romeo team get away; the team are Ivanowski (32), Callingham (43), Campari (35) and Headlam (41). The three-litre-class cars wait on the right-hand side of the track for their start

The following year's TT had official works entries from Mercedes-Benz, Alfa Romeo, Bugatti, Lagonda, Alvis, Austin, Riley and Frazer-Nash with drivers to match. The race belonged to German Rudi Caracciola whose 7.1-litre supercharged Mercedes-Benz SS proved the fastest car on the track. In wet and treacherous conditions, the German drove what he described as one of his hardest-ever races to beat his rivals and the handicappers, finishing 2 m 8 s in front of Giuseppe Campari's 1½-litre Alfa Romeo. The first-ever TT fatality occurred when a breakdown crew was struck by an out-of-control Triumph.

Caracciola was disqualified from participating in the 1930 race, his Mercedes' supercharger being declared too large. The race was an Alfa Romeo benefit with the 1750 models of Tazio Nuvolari, Giuseppe Campari and Achille Varzi taking a superb 1–2–3 victory. In 1931 Alfa Romeo entered once more, although Bugatti withdrew his new 4.9-litre cars following a disastrous outing at Le Mans. The Italians lost the race, their drivers more intent on blowing each other off than settling down to a suitable pace in the quest of victory over the handicappers, and ultimately Baconin Borzacchini's 2.3-litre Alfa Romeo Sports 8C finished over a minute behind Norman Black's coolly conducted 746 cc supercharged MG Midget C-type. Few big cars entered in 1932. Battling for the lead former motor-cycle ace Freddie Dixon hit the kerb, his Riley Nine vaulting over a hedge into retirement. Winner was C. R. Whitcroft's Riley Nine. In 1933 the race was enlivened by a titanic struggle between two MGs, the 1100 cc K3 Magnette of Tazio Nuvolari and Hugh Hamilton's 750 cc J4 Midget. It was resolved in the Italian's favour.

For 1934 the RAC tried to revert more to the original format of the race. They demanded cars must carry 'full touring trim' and banned superchargers and, despite much criticism, received a representative entry. Charlie Dobson's 1.3-litre MG Magnette NE-type conquered Eddie Hall's 3.7-litre Rolls-Bentley by a scant 17 s after over six hours' racing. In 1935 (when the race was run under a national permit owing to a mistake over international dates)—a year in which three Singers crashed independently at the same corner through steering failure—Freddie Dixon's famous 1½-litre Riley triumphed. The 1936 race was overshadowed when J.

Chambers, driving an 1100 cc Riley, lost control at a fast left-hander at Newtownards and plunged into the crowd, killing eight and seriously injuring another fifteen. The race ran its course, Dixon sharing his Riley with Charlie Dobson to beat Eddie Hall's Rolls-Bentley.

The tragedy meant a change of venue. Donington was lengthened to 3.125 miles and filled the gap for 1937 and 1938, but in many eyes it was not considered the ideal circuit. French victories resulted: the two Darracqs of Gianfranco Comotti and René Le Bègue triumphed in 1937, the following year it was Delage's turn, Louis Gérard winning by over 3 minutes.

Following World War II the Tourist Trophy was revived in Northern Ireland on the 7.42-mile Dundrod circuit west of Belfast. Narrow, twisty, with steep banks often obstructing views, exposed to winds and not boasting many spectator amenities, Dundrod was potentially dangerous. But it was the only true road circuit the RAC could turn to and for drivers it was a real test of their skill. In 1950 a representative entry of British sports cars raced in pouring rain and the TT showed up the true talent of a young British driver named Stirling Moss. On the eve of his 21st birthday, Moss was handling a powerful sports car for the first time, journalist-cum-racing driver Tommy Wisdom's Jaguar XK 120. Moss dominated the conditions and the handicappers, beating Peter Whitehead's XK 120 and the Frazer-Nash Le Mans Replica of Bob Gerard. He also earned a contract to join the Jaguar works team, thereafter repeating his victory—in much better conditions—in a factory-entered C-type in 1951.

In 1952 the TT was cancelled owing to lack of entries and the following year the RAC delegated the organisation of the race to the Ulster Automobile Club. Resurfacing of the circuit made it very abrasive, with the result tyres quickly perished under the strain. Fortunately wet weather eased the strain in the early stages, but as the track dried rubber-consumption increased. Among the victims were the Jaguars, so Aston Martin scored a 1–2 victory with the DB3s of Peter Collins/Pat Griffith and Reg Parnell/Eric Thomson taking over 9½ hours to cover the 823 miles.

In 1954 Ferrari, Lancia, Maserati and DB-Panhard entries gave the race an international flavour. It proved a triumph for the handicappers, the 750 cc DB-Panhard of Frenchmen Paul Armagnac/Gérard Laureau beating the 3-litre Ferrari Monza 750 of Mike Hawthorn/Maurice Trintignant by 35 s after 94 laps—or 7 hours' racing. And only a further 23 s in arrears was the 2-litre Maserati A6GCS of Luigi Musso/Sergio Mantovani.

In 1955—Golden Jubilee year, but only the 22nd race—a terrific entry was obtained. By now sports cars were out-and-out racing machinery thanks to loosely composed international regulations, and for the first time since 1922 the TT was to be a straightforward scratch race. Entries came from Jaguar, Ferrari, Mercedes-Benz, Maserati, Aston Martin, Triumph, Kieft, Porsche, MG, Lotus, Cooper, Elva, DB, Panhard and Stanguellini. The mixture ranged from 3½-litre cars to minute 750 cc devices and some road-going cars were mixed with pure racing machinery. It was a potentially dangerous mixture for Dundrod. The year had already been overshadowed by the Le Mans catastrophe—that was sparked by cars of differing potential on narrow roads—and the fatal accident to twice World Champion Alberto Ascari.

On lap 2 it happened. Jim Mayers' Cooper crashed and caught fire, six other cars being involved in the *mêlée*. Mayers was killed, so was young Connaught driver Bill Smith, while Ken Wharton was seriously burned. Later Richard Mainwaring overturned his

Elva and was killed, adding to the gloom which overshadowed the strenuous fight put up by Mike Hawthorn and Desmond Titterington in their Jaguar D-type against the might of the Mercedes team. Within minutes of the finish the Jaguar blew up, leaving the Mercedes-Benz 300SLRs of Stirling Moss/John Fitch, Juan Manuel Fangio/Karl Kling and Wolfgang von Trips/André Simon to claim an easy 1–2–3 victory.

For safety reasons the Tourist Trophy was never run at Dundrod again. The race lay dormant until 1958 when it was revived at Goodwood, the 2.40-mile Sussex circuit proving to be its base until 1964. Run as a four-hour race, the first Goodwood TT was organised by the British Automobile Racing Club on behalf of the RAC. With little opposition, the works Aston Martin DBR1/300s of Stirling Moss/Tony Brooks, Roy Salvadory/Jack Brabham and Carroll Shelby/Stuart Lewis-Evans cantered to an easy 1–2–3 victory. The following year saw a much-improved entry and a full six-hours' duration. Ferrari and Porsche vied with Aston Martin for honours in the World Sports Car Championship. Aston Martin seemed set for victory when the unexpected happened. In for a routine pit-stop, the leading Moss/Salvadory car caught fire and the Aston Martin pits—including lap charts, tyres, tools, drivers' gear and even the team manager's briefcase loaded with money—were badly burned. The day was saved when a private owner handed his pit over to the works and Moss requisitioned another team car to win the race and clinch the championship from Ferrari and Porsche.

Once again going back to 'basics', the TT reverted to a GT car event. Stirling Moss, at the wheel of a Ferrari 250GT, won in 1960, listening to the BBC broadcast on the car radio as he did so. He repeated the dose the following year, winning his seventh TT and his fourth in succession, drivers being Innes Ireland and Graham Hill respectively. In 1964, although the race was a crucial round in the GT Championship, the race was also opened to sports-prototypes and Hill won in a 4-litre Ferrari 330P.

The RAC took over the organisation of the TT once more in 1965, moving the race to Cheshire's 2.761-mile Oulton Park circuit. They ran the race in two two-hour parts and opened it to giant, 'big-banger' sports cars as well as GT machinery. It was an event of controversy as the winner's flag fell between the two major contestants for victory in each heat, giving a strange result in that winner Denny Hulme's 2-litre Brabham BT8-Climax, which covered 138 laps, had a slower average speed than second man David Hobbs' 4.7-litre Lola T70-Ford, which was credited with 137 laps. Hulme won a similar-format race in 1966, nursing Sid Taylor's 5.9-litre Lola T70 Mk 2-Chevrolet home after virtually all the other 'big-bangers' retired.

Since the late 1960s the race has suffered from the whims of circuit owners, none of whom were truly fond of long-distance racing. With the RAC not liking Sunday races, the major sports-car races promoted at Brands Hatch could not be allocated the Tourist Trophy title. The race remained at Oulton Park until 1969. In 1967, as a round of the European Touring Car Challenge, it provided Italian Andrea de Adamich with victory in an Autodelta-entered Alfa Romeo Giulia GTA. The following year it was back to sports cars when Denny Hulme earned his third TT win in Sid Taylor's 5-litre Lola T70 Mk 3-Chevrolet. A year later a similar-format race was halted prematurely when Paul Hawkins lost control of his 5-litre Lola T70 Mk 3B-Chevrolet, crashed in flames and was killed. The track was blocked and the race verdict given to Trevor Taylor (Lola T70 Mk 3B-Chevrolet) who had been leading prior to the tragedy. The brave Taylor had attempted to extinguish the flames and rescue Hawkins.

From 1970 the TT was held at Silverstone on the 2.927-mile ex-airfield circuit, each time for touring cars. Brian Muir's 5-litre Chevrolet Camaro Z28 took the honours in 1970, there was no race the following year but in 1972 Jochen Mass/Dieter Glemser won in their German Ford Capri RS2600. BMWs triumphed in 1973, Derek Bell/Harald Ertl being the winning Anglo-Austrian crew in a 3.5-litre BMW 3.0 CSL entered by the German Alpina tuning firm. In 1974 the race was run for slightly-modified touring cars, Stuart Graham's 5.7-litre Chevrolet Camaro Z28 taking a comfortable victory which helped gain him the Tarmac British Racing Champion award. For 1975 a race along slightly altered lines was planned with more modifications permitted.   MK

Above: Frank Gardner's Chevrolet Camaro that proved so quick in the 1973 British Touring Car Championship takes on the works cars of BMW and Ford in the '73 event at Silverstone. Frank's privately entered SCA Freight car had to give best to an Alpina 3.5-litre BMW after tyre troubles

A GIANT FROM JAPAN

Since World War II, the Toyota company has grown into a major motor manufacturing concern with sales outlets all over the world

SAKICHI TOYODA, a world famous inventor and designer of automatic looms, had always conducted his business with a keen eye to the future. He anticipated earlier than most in Japan that the production of automobiles would eventually become a major industry and in September 1933, began to make preparations for active participation in car manufacture.

Combining available income from patent licensing fees for his automatic looms with profits from their sale, he added an automobile department to his Toyoda Automatic Loom Works company. Shortly afterwards he handed his business and the motor company to his eldest son, Kiichiro Toyoda.

In May 1935 the first prototype test car, designated the Toyota A-1, was completed. One of the first cars to be built in Japan, it was powered by a 3400 cc 45 hp unit which the company had designed and produced themselves. A prototype of the Toyota G-1 truck appeared in October 1935 and went into full production shortly afterwards.

Derivatives of the A-1 motor car appeared in the pre-war years, mainly the AA four door sedan and the AB Tourer, both of which were powered by a six cylinder in-line overhead valve engine which developed 65 hp at 3000 rpm.

In August 1937, Toyota Motor Co, Ltd, was established under the presidency of Risaburo Toyoda, with Kiichiro Toyoda as vice-president. Production proved to run smoothly but sales of the unproven product proved a tremendous challenge. Salesmen had to deal with an untested market, an unpredictable factor which made sales a more formidable obstacle than production. But that year Kiichiro Toyoda, who later succeeded Risaburo Toyoda to become the second president of Toyota, met Shotaro Kamiya (current president of Toyota Motor Sales Co, Ltd), who at that time was heading the sales department of General Motors, Japan. Kamiya was soon invited to join Toyota and given control of all the company's sales efforts, a move which was to have dramatic effects on the company's expansion.

In November 1938, the company's first independent vehicle factory was built in Koromo City and production began. This facility is now Toyota Motor Company's Honsha Plant. That year a C version of the AA and AB models was introduced and the following

Below: the brutal-looking Toyota 2000GT of 1966; its power unit was a two-litre, six-cylinder, twin-cam unit.

In 1954 the company took the fairly unusual step of buying a driving school, the Nippon Driving School of Tachikawa City. Their intention was clear: to promote vehicle sales using every method and technique at their disposal. The following year Toyota unveiled the Toyota Crown which, fitted with a 1453 cc overhead valve, four cylinder engine, had a three speed synchromeshed gearbox, column change, hydraulic brakes and hypoid final drive. With annual car production now heading towards the 10,000 mark, Toyota established the Toyota Used Car Sales Co, Ltd, to provide financial aid to used car dealers and conduct research on problems in used car marketing.

1957 saw the introduction of the Toyota Corona, a 1000 cc four seater and the establishment of Toyota Motor Sales USA Inc, with a capital of $1 million. The Toyota Crown, which was the only model exported in 1957, made little impact on the market and the Corona, which followed in 1958, was equally little noticed by the American car buying public. No further export effort was made in the USA by Toyota until 1965, when the New Corona was introduced. Sixty-four hundred were sold in the first six months and 16,000 in a full year's operation. Sales in the USA rose to 33,000 in 1967 and to 67,000 in 1968. In 1969 sales of Toyota cars in America of 180,600 gave them second place to Volkswagen in the importers' league.

Toyota's return to the USA in 1965 was a deliberate move to fill a gap in the market which careful research had identified. Shoji Hattori, head of Toyota's Ameri-

year it was joined by the newly styled AE model.

Production of cars by Toyota in the immediate prewar years amounted to 1320 units; while truck production had risen from 20 units in 1935 to 11,981 in 1939. This bias was a result of a Japanese government ruling that insisted on priority to truck production.

Between 1940 and 1944 Toyota produced only 600 cars, though a number of experimental designs were also developed. At the end of 1945, the Occupation Forces permitted monthly production of 1500 trucks, but enforced a tight ban on the production of passenger cars. While engaging in the production of trucks, however, Toyota engineers continued to work on designs for the future, particularly of small-engined models.

The ban was lifted in October 1949 but post war economic conditions in Japan had not improved to a point where full scale production could begin. The company's structure was further rationalised in April 1950 and an independent retail unit, Toyota Motor Sales Co, Ltd, was formed. In the first five years under this new structure Toyota car production rose from 1470 in 1951 to 3572 in 1953 and 7403 in 1955.

Toyota had designed and produced their first postwar model as early as 1947, the SA, which was a two door sedan powered by a 27 bhp engine and was the first of the company's models to carry the Toyopet trade mark. When the model ceased production in May 1952, 215 units had been built and sold. In February 1952, Toyota sold 100 Model FX trucks to Brazil and began their post-war export programme.

Above: the little Publica S that rivalled the small Hondas. It was powered by a twin-cylinder 800 cc engine

Above: the three-litre, 150 bhp Century Sedan

Left: another version of the Publica, this being a hardtop

can operation, had instituted a complete study of what the market wanted, including interviews with dealers as well as car customers. Japanese engineers turned the results into the New Corona, a two door hardtop. Meanwhile foreign car manufacturers' export activities in the USA were closely studied as a basis for new sales and service policies.

The cars Toyota offered in the USA were compact but with all the comfort and attractive extras which customers had requested. The cars were low cost, selling at a premium of between £120 and £150 above those in Japan, with lively performance, good handling, modern Detroit-style interiors and with accessories fitted such as air conditioning, stereo players and FM radios.

Equally Toyota appeared on the West Coast of America at a time when the American car market as a whole was booming. Initial concentration by Toyota was in Los Angeles and the advertising campaigns brought out the fun and versatility of the foreign car, but there was no emphasis on its Japanese origin. The low price and economic motoring were additional themes and they proved successful in channelling the potential demand for second and third cars to Toyota dealers.

Toyota's emphasis on after-sales service was, however, to prove the real motivating force for sales in America. Before beginning to sell their first cars in the Southern California area, the company established 65 dealers and a huge parts depot. Only when sales in this area were firmly established did the operation expand and, even then, sales expanded only in conjunction with the development of a satisfactory parts and service network. As a result, by 1971, Toyota had 1260 dealers in the USA and six computerised parts depots. This was to continue to be their plan of campaign in other export markets.

The Motomachi plant, Toyota's first assembly plant exclusively for the manufacture of passenger cars in Japan, began operating in 1959. It was here that the production of Corona and Crown models was initiated. Two years later the company launched their 700 Series called the Publica. Powered by air cooled 700 cc engines, the four seaters were the smallest in the Toyota range.

By June 1962 Toyota had produced one million vehicles since their inception in 1935. Later that same year the company established the Toyota Motor Thailand Co., Ltd., and began work on a car assembly plant in that country which was completed in February 1964.

Above: the 95 bhp 1600 cc Corono coupé 1600S

Below: the Crown Super Deluxe Sedan

Bottom: the Toyota 1600GT of the mid 1960s

Toyota exported the first of their products to Western Europe in 1962, beginning with a shipment to Greece. In the following year shipments were sent to Denmark and Holland.

These exports were followed in 1964 by further shipments to Sweden, Finland, Norway and Switzerland. Shipments to the UK, Belgium and France followed in 1966.

In April 1965 Toyota's cumulative vehicle production passed the two million mark and the Kamigo plant was inaugurated for the production of engines and transmissions. In the December of the following year, the Takaoka Plant was constructed lifting the total production capacity to a monthly rate of 30,000 Corollas. By that year Toyota were producing 316,189 cars and 587,539 commercial vehicles annually pushing their cumulative production figure to over the three million mark.

Toyota also established a subsidiary in Peru in 1966 and reached an agreement on an overall business tie-up with Hino Motors Ltd. A similar business tie-up was reached with the Daihatsu Kogyo Co, Ltd, the following year.

Following the launch of the Toyota Century in November 1967, the Corona models were given 1½-litre 74 bhp and 1.6-litre 95 bhp engines, while the Crown series of models had six and eight cylinder units. This latter engine, a 115 bhp V8, provided the top of the Toyota range in 1967. That year there were also two sports models available on the Japanese market, powered by twin overhead camshaft engines of either four or six cylinders. Toyota were also marketing the Landcruiser, a four wheel drive vehicle using their 3.9-litre push rod six cylinder truck engine.

In January 1968 Toyota invested in Australian Motor Industries Ltd., and completed their Miyoshi Plant in Japan which was to produce chassis parts and launched the Corona Mark II. By this time Toyota were producing 659,189 passenger cars a year and 1,097,405 commercial vehicles bringing their cumulative production figure to nearly five million. This was also the year in which the company launched their first car export ship, Dai-Ichi Toyota Maru, which had a gross tonnage of 12,600 and a capacity for 1200 Coronas. Towards the end of 1969 the company exported their millionth vehicle, and six months later, the millionth Corolla.

In December 1970 completion of the Tsutsumi Plant for the production of Celica and Carina models took place. The Celica had a 1588 cc 115 bhp four cylinder unit, front disc brakes and a five speed all-synchromesh gearbox, while the Carina was powered by either a 1.4

Above: Toyota's answer to the Land-Rover, the Land Cruiser

litre or 1.6 litre four cylinder unit and featured live axle and coil rear suspension. With the completion of the Tsutsumi Plant in Toyota City, the company's annual production capacity reached the two million unit mark. Passenger car production that year passed the one million mark for the first time with 1,068,321 units and when added to the commercial vehicle production figure for that year of 1,609,190 units brought Toyota's cumulative production figure to just under the eight million mark. Toyota Motor Co, Ltd, has ranked third in vehicle production among all automotive manufacturers in the world since 1969.

In January 1972 Toyota's cumulative vehicle production passed the 10 million mark and the company took a share in Canadian Motor Industries Holding Ltd. That year the Publica was available with a 790 cc air-cooled engine and a 1 litre or 1.2 litre water cooled four cylinder engine; Corollas were available with either 1.2, 1.4 or 1.6 litre engines, with a five speed gearbox employed on the high performance SR Coupé; the Carina had 1.4 or 1.6 litre power units while the Carina 1600GT had twin carburettors; the Coronas had 1707 cc or 1858 cc engines with transmission through four speed boxes while the top of the range models had five speed boxes to transmit the power from their twin cam 2-litre 140 bhp units; the Celicas continued to have twin overhead camshaft 1600 engines while the Crown was only available with 2-litre, 2.3 litre or 2.6 litre versions of six cylinder power units; and the Century's output was increased to 170 bhp.

In 1972, the cumulative sales of the Toyota Corolla on the Japanese market passed the two million mark, and the one millionth export unit of the same car was produced. It was also the year that Toyota donated $1 million to Harvard University.

A year later saw the company introduce two new lines of small cars, the Starlet and a revamped Corona. Conventional in design the Starlet was available at launch in two door coupé and four door sedan models and was based on the power and transmission units of the Publica which had earlier grown to a 1000 and 1200 cc model. The Corona range for that year came with two alternative overhead valve 1.6-litre engines, a single overhead camshaft 1.8-litre four cylinder, a

single overhead camshaft electronic fuel injection two litre unit and a twin camshaft 2 litre GT unit. Five mile-per-hour crash bumpers were introduced that year on the Corona.

In January Toyota announced their intention of spending 23 billion Yen on safety and control research though this was reduced by 10 per cent in the June of the same year. That year Toyota also bought a Wankel licence from Audi NSU Auto Union AG and began work on the Shimoyaama Plant which is to manufacture exhaust emission control devices and related parts and components.

Already hard at work on safety and environmental protection systems, Toyota doubled their budget to 52 billion Yen in April 1974. In May of that year the 15 millionth Toyota passenger vehicle came off the production line and the company made their 1½ millionth sale in the USA. In the August of the same year an agreement was signed with the Kenya government for work to commence on the local assembly of motor vehicles. A revised version of the Toyota Crown was launched in the October of that year and a month later a German subsidiary began importing and distributing cars in Western Germany.

That year Toyota manufactured 1,484,737 passenger cars and 2,114,980 commercial vehicles bringing their cumulative vehicle production to 16,409,270 units.

Since 1966 Toyota have increased their budget for research and development into safety measures sixfold and the number of staff involved in safety and research development has been increased three times. Research and development work on safety and anti-pollution projects is mainly conducted at Toyota's Higashi-Fuji Technical Centre, a huge 240 million square metre site inaugurated in 1967 at the foot of Mt. Fuji. Within the centre's grounds can be found an automobile performance testing laboratory, a gas purification research laboratory, a skid testing road, a collision test ground and an all-weather test room.

Toyota engineers have produced several major contributions to vehicle safety, some of which have already been employed on certain Toyota models. Their air bag system is designed to protect vehicle passengers from the effects of an accident by functioning to minimise crash impact a split-second before actual collision. A key feature of this system is the built-in radar sensor which is responsible for the automatic operation of the air bag in a crash situation. The Toyota OK-Monitor (Electro Sensor Panel) automatically monitors every part which functions on a car, during actual driving or when stationary. Changes in all major functions are

Below: in the British Touring Car Championship Group One series in England in 1975, the Celica GT proved immensely quick in the up-to-1600 cc class. Here, Win Percy rounds the hairpin at Mallory Park, near Leicester

Below: Toyotas have not always been up-to-date motor cars as this early Crown Custom shows

Bottom: the Corona 2000Mk II is, altogether, a more striking and European design

Below: the Corolla 1200RS Coupé

Right: the Corona 1800

Left: the Carina 1600 Super Deluxe

Above: the Celica 1600ST Coupé

Below: the Corona Deluxe 1500

indicated by pilot lamps. Terminal sensors are mounted extensively throughout the vehicle to provide continuous monitoring.

Other safety developments at Toyota are incorporated in their latest Experimental Safety Vehicle, among the many being four wheel disc brakes fitted with an electronic skid control system, a single-wire multiplex network system which abolishes complicated wiring by channelling impulses through a single wire network linked to a mini-computer, an air bag system, and a 10 mph crash-resistant bumper system. Ten Toyota ESVs were delivered to the Japanese Government in November 1973, one of which was subsequently given to the American Department of Transportation.

In the field of anti-pollution, Toyota's cumulative 45-fold since 1966 and the personnel engaged in the programme has expanded almost 13 times during the same period. This mammoth investment has enabled Toyota to satisfy the Japanese Government's 1975 auto emission regulations and has resulted in the development of an anti-pollution device which employs catalytic converters of a type peculiar to Toyota.

Among Toyota developments for the future are the development of a practical gas turbine engine, a programme which has been under way since 1964 and which aims at producing a range of gas turbine engines from 33 hp to 350 hp. Work is also being carried out on the development of an electric vehicle suitable for urban transport. Prototypes already developed will carry five passengers at a maximum speed of 90 Km/hr and work is proceeding on achieving a 200 Kilometre driving range between charges.

While conducting intensive automotive research and development, Toyota are also actively working on control of the traffic environment. A significant achievement in this area is the Toyota Multi-functional Automobile Communication System (MAC) which is designed to simplify driving, promote traffic safety, solve traffic congestion and controlling problems, add to motoring convenience, and give drivers the advantage of a comprehensive communications system. The MAC system is composed of four basic sub systems: a car telephone unit, a computerised intersection information unit, a running information receiver unit and an emergency information unit.

For the future, Toyota plans to introduce an energy and resource conserving automobile in terms of fuel and material consumption, production processes and recyclability. The proposed vehicle will be designed to be popular and inexpensive and will employ lightweight materials with a pollution free engine and improved fuel consumption. Toyota have already initiated a programme to stimulate the production of reusable parts and this is moving ahead on four fronts: methods of collecting used parts, development of production techniques for reusable parts, establishment of quality standards for reusable parts and economic and other considerations. Similarly an ambitious programme to design a car in which the products and materials can be reused or recycled is also underway with the fundamental goal being the design of a car which is safe, easy to disassemble, the parts of which can be easily replaced and the component materials of which are easy to salvage and recycle. This is an ambitious programme indeed.   BJ

Above: the mass-production Toyota Corolla assembly line at Takaoka

CELICA GT

The Toyota Celica was introduced in 1970 as a competitor to the Fiat 124 Coupé and the MGB GT. In shape, it looked like a shortened Ford Mustang, being a two-door coupé with a low front and a bulky rear end.

By 1975, the Celica was available with a variety of engine options from a single-camshaft 1400 cc to a 145 bhp, two-litre lusty twin cam. This version was not available in England, though.

So, the top of the Celica range in Great Britain for 1975 is the GT, a 1588 cc 124 bhp twin-cam that gives little away to its larger relatives.

In 124 bhp form, with the standard five-speed gearbox, the car has a top speed of 115 mph and accelerates from 0–60 mph in 9 secs. An overall fuel consumption of 24 mpg can be returned.

The Celica's front suspension is independent by MacPherson struts, coil springs and an anti-roll bar, while the rear is live by a rigid axle, located by four trailing links and a Panhard rod, coil springs and telescopic dampers. Braking is taken care of by dual-circuit, servo-assisted front discs and rear drums, while the steering is of the recirculating-ball type.

The car's interior is smart and sporty in the GT style, complete with the usual host of dials, radio, a centre console and high-back seats.

ENGINE Front-mounted, water-cooled straight-four. 85 mm (3.35 in) bore × 70 mm (2.76 in) stroke 1588 cc (96.9 cu in). Maximum power (SAE) 124 bhp at 6400 rpm; maximum torque (SAE) 113 lb ft at 5200 rpm. Cast-iron cylinder block and light-alloy head. Compression ratio 9.8:1. 2 valves per cylinder operated direct by twin overhead camshafts. Twin Solex 40 PHH twin-choke side-draught carburetters.

TRANSMISSION Single-dry-plate clutch and 5-speed manual gearbox. Ratios, 1st 3.587, 2nd 2.022, 3rd 1.384, 4th 1, 5th 0.861, rev 3.484:1. Hypoid-bevel final drive. Ratio 4.100.

CHASSIS Integral.

SUSPENSION Front—Independent by MacPherson struts, coil springs and an anti-roll bar. Rear—non-independent by a rigid axle, located by four links and a Panhard rod, coil springs and telescopic dampers.

STEERING Recirculating ball. Turns from lock to lock 3.50.

BRAKES Dual circuit, servo-assisted front discs and rear drums.

WHEELS 5 inJ × 13 in steel.

TYRES 165HR × 13.

DIMENSIONS AND WEIGHT Wheelbase 95.47 in; track—front 50.39 in, rear—50.59 in; length 163.98 in; width 62.99 in; height 51.57 in; ground clearance 6.89 in; dry weight 2106 lb; turning circle between walls 34.1 ft; fuel tank capacity 11 gals.

BODY 2-door, 4–5 seats.

ELECTRICAL EQUIPMENT 12 volt, 35 ah battery.

PERFORMANCE Maximum speed 115 mph. Acceleration 0–60 mph 9 secs. Fuel consumption approximately 24 mpg.

CORONA MK II

In an attempt to boost her ailing economy following World War II, Japan flooded the world markets with products which, not to put too fine a point on it, were of inferior quality. Consequently, the words 'made in Japan' were regarded with suspicion for many years.

Japanese technology, however, has made such great strides that it is now a recognised leader in many fields, including electronics, photography and motor-cycle manufacture.

The Toyota Corona Mark II models, introduced into Britain in 1974, are good examples of Japanese efforts to overcome the stigma once associated with Japanese products.

The Corona Mark II range consists of the 2000 four-door saloon, the 2000 four-door automatic and the 2000-five-door estate, and all are powered by a single-overhead-camshaft, four-cylinder engine of 1968 cc. It produces 119 bhp at 5500 rpm and 129 lb ft of torque at 3600.

The cars are well designed, well built and all can accommodate five adults in complete comfort.

The manual versions are fitted with four-speed, all synchromesh floor-shift gearboxes, while the automatic version uses a Toyota/Borg Warner three-speed unit. The clutch, in all cases, is a nine-inch diameter single-dry-plate unit.

Steering is by recirculating ball, while braking is taken care of by discs at the front and drums at the rear. Suspension is by coil springs, double wishbones and anti-roll bar at the front and a live axle and coil springs (progressive leaf springs for the estate) at the rear.

ENGINE Front mounted, water cooled straight four. 88.5 mm (3.48 in) bore × 80.0 mm (3.15 in) stroke = 1968 cc (120.1 cu in). Maximum power (SAE) 119 bhp at 5500 rpm; maximum torque (SAE) 129 lb ft at 3600 rpm. Cast-iron cylinder block with aluminium-alloy head. Compression ratio 8.5:1. 5 main bearings. 2 valves per cylinder operated, via rockers, by a single overhead camshaft. 1 downdraught twin-barrel carburetter with automatic choke.

TRANSMISSION Single-dry-plate clutch and four-speed manual gearbox (2000 4-door and 5-door estate) or Toyota/Borg-Warner 3-speed automatic transmission (2000 4-door automatic). Ratios (manual) 1st 3.578, 2nd 2.081, 3rd 1.397, 4th 1.000, rev 4.399:1. Ratios (automatic) 1st 2.450, 2nd 1.450, 3rd 1.000, rev 2.220:1. Semi-floating hypoid final drive. Ratio 3.700:1 (saloons), 3.909:1 (estate).

CHASSIS Integral

SUSPENSION Front—independent by coil springs, double wishbones and anti-roll bar. Rear—live axle located by five links, coil springs (saloons) or live axle, progressive leaf springs (estate).

STEERING Recirculating ball, with collapsible column

BRAKES Servo-assisted discs (10.5 in) front, drums (9.53 in) rear.

WHEELS 5 in × 14 in steel.

TYRES 165 × 14 radial ply.

DIMENSIONS AND WEIGHT Wheelbase 101.8 in; track—front 53.5 in, rear 52.95 in; length 170.3 in (saloons), 171.3 (estate); width 64 in; height 55.1 in (saloons), 55.7 in (estate); ground clearance 6.9 in; kerb weight 2485 lb (manual saloon), 2520 lb (automatic saloon), 2530 lb (estate); tank capacity 13.2 gals (saloons) or 12.1 gals (estate); turning circle between walls 34 ft.

BODY 4-door, 5-seater saloon, or 5-door, 5-seater estate.

PERFORMANCE Maximum speed 100 mph (manual saloon), 98 mph (automatic saloon) or 100 mph (estate). Acceleration from 0–50 mph, approximately 9.0 secs (all models). Fuel consumption 23.6 mpg.

KEEPING MOTOR VEHICLES ON THE MOVE

The problem of traffic congestion grows with every new car made. Consequently, road builders and designers must constantly plan for the future

THE FOUNDER OF BRITAIN'S road system must be regarded as Julius Caesar. Most of the routes tramped by his Roman legions, and by subsequent militia, were accepted for generations as the best way from A to B, and many remain in use today, the original foundations several feet below the tarmac. These were not inconsequential tracks either—parts of Watling Street and Ermine Street measured 80 feet between drainage ditches. All along these routes masons chiselled and set milestones, hundreds of which survive as testimony to the Romans' recognition of the essential nature for good traffic information.

After the Romans departed a great many of their roads fell into disuse, and though some major routes remained, travellers on them had to trust to the sun, stars, and instinct for direction. The first recorded post-Roman signs were noted by a German traveller in Kent in 1595, and a hundred years later signposts were still rare enough to be accorded special mention in Celia Fienne's well-known journal of her far-ranging travels through England.

By this time traffic control was a feature of London life—one of the earliest enactments was that of Charles I in 1635 prohibiting the use of hired coaches in the London vicinity unless the passenger was travelling at least three miles out of the town. Not only was the short journey banned, but there was a levy—the coach owner was required to keep four horses for the King's use. This edict, according to one contemporary account, reducing the number of coaches operating in London from 6000 to 60. But by the following year, 600 were operating again. Evasion of traffic laws is as old as the laws themselves.

In the latter half of the 17th century and the first half of the 18th, Britain adopted a turnpike system. The first, a levy on the use of the Great North Road in 1663, was scandalously pricey at the time—one shilling for five miles. The turnpikes were not liked—breaking a tollgate was punishable by death, and a 1749 turnpike riot in Bristol lasted a fortnight and only ended when the Army moved in. But the effect on communications they had was dramatic. Even by 1713 it was recorded that coaches could cover one hundred miles a day, which was four times the previously accepted pace. The turnpikes did wonders for signposting too. Each of the four hundred or so Turnpike Acts which created the new network during the first half of the 18th century demanded systematic signing.

The turnpikes chided memories too—in 1586 the Master of Trinity Hall, Cambridge, had left £1600 in trust, the interest to be spent on mending the road between Cambridge and Barking. In 1725 they got around to doing something about it, and six-foot high stone signs were placed along the road at five-mile intervals. Unfortunately for most of the travellers of the day, all the mileages were cut in Roman numerals. Each sign, including cutting, cost £2 12s.

Meanwhile the congestion which had angered Charles I was again choking the metropolis. A 1722 order of the Lord Mayor's Court provided for three 'able persons' to patrol London Bridge to divert all traffic approaching from the Southwark end to take to the west side of the bridge, and all that coming on from the City end to hold the east side in order to avoid 'the great inconvenienced and mischiefs which happen by the disorderly driving of cars, carts, coaches and other carriages' (Cars were small commercial carts drawn by one or two horses).

Below: a street scene in Milan on 3 August 1926, with pedestrians clearly outnumbering their wheeled counterparts *Right:* in contrast, vehicular congestion in Palermo in 1970

This appears to be the first recorded instance of driving on the left in Britain, and of traffic direction by specially appointed officers of a court. In addition this order laid down the first known vehicle regulations as well—limitations were placed on the weight of loads, which had to be related to the number of horses drawing the wagon, and narrow wheels which cut into the roads were penalised by extra tolls.

Thomas Telford was one of the pioneers of traffic engineering, while Macadam and others concentrated on carriageway improvements. From 1815 or so, Telford's roads incorporated levels and general construction aimed at reducing minimum necessary tractive effort, plus intelligent routing to shorten distances where possible. The minimising of gradients and reduction of road surface friction became the benchmark for road engineers for several decades. One of Telford's associates, John Macneill, used a crude dynamometer attached to carriage shafts to measure road/vehicle friction and used the results to compare the economics of five different proposals for the improvement of the Stowe Hill Valley in Northamptonshire in 1830.

The first omnibuses had begun to replace short-stage coaches in London in the late 1820s, and the growth of the railways subsequently superseded the turnpikes. 1858 and 1859 saw the closure of the last two important out-of-London coach services, the Derby Dilly to Manchester and the Quicksilver to Plymouth. Only one service remained, the daily three-horse coach between the Old Bell in Holborn and Amersham, which ran until 1890. The turnpike trusts went bankrupt. They had received £1.5 million in 1837. By 1840 their debts totalled £9 million. More than 20,000 miles of roads fell into disrepair, and in 1878 most of the thousand trusts were disbanded by the Locomotive and Highways Act.

The growth of the railways may have robbed the roads of all but local traffic, but it generated vast new amounts of town traffic. The railway also inspired the first road signal. In December 1868, at the junction of London's Parliament Street and Bridge Street, a mechanical signal was set up at the suggestion of Mr J. P. Knight, of the South Eastern Railway. Mounted on a 23 ft high standard were three semaphore arms operated by a handle. When they were raised, all traffic stopped to allow pedestrians—particularly MPs—to cross the road. At night a gas lantern illuminated red and green coloured glass panels for the same purpose. The system worked—but fell into disuse after an explosion, and an objection by the Commissioner of Police over the cost of the gas on his budget.

Apart from specific local orders, the only law regulating traffic generally had been the Sunday Observance acts of the 16th century. During the early 1800s, street-keepers—widely known as beadles—operated a vague control at some junctions. When the police were formed in 1829 they inherited the job. The 1835 Highway Act confirmed the drive-on-the-left rule and also made speeding—it was officially described as 'furious driving'—an offence. Another act of 1839 gave London police powers to regulate traffic on special occasions and in special places and later acts reinforced these powers. It was soon accepted that the police should regulate traffic flow at junctions and keep them clear for pedestrians.

In 1865 the original Locomotives and Highways Act—later known as the Red Flag Act—had imposed the first speed controls on the steam-propelled waggons which were beginning to appear to the chagrin of a horse-orientated public. The act demanded that every road locomotive have at least one driver, one stoker, and a man walking ahead to warn oncoming traffic and help

The police forces of the world are an integral part of traffic control and, whether armed with 'walkie-talkies', as the London policeman, *left*, or just a whistle as the New York officer, *below*, they help to keep the traffic moving

at the junction of Gracechurch Street and Cornhill, in the City of London, in 1932. Ironically, just as the Westminster semaphore came to grief through gas, so did this first modern signal set—gas seepage got into the electro-magnetic relay mechanism, and when the signals were switched on, a contact-strip vehicle detector blew up! Nonetheless, this system was the first use of a computer technique—and computers were to play a massive role in the future.

The London Traffic Act of 1924 gave the police some traffic management powers and also tied together the 37

control frightened horses. Maximum speed permitted was 2 mph in town and 4 mph in open country. Thirty years later the first real 'horseless carriages'—some steam, some electric, some petrol-driven—clattered onto the streets. Amid great controversy the 1896 'Emancipation Act' recognised a new class of light locomotive, relieved the new-fangled contraptions of the need to be preceded by a man with a red flag, and permitted a speed of 12 mph. The Motor Car Act of 1903 raised the speed limit to 20 mph and imposed registration marks on cars and licences on drivers.

There was during this period a great clash in towns between the old and new types of traffic. Some saw the motor car as the salvation of the city. In his Motor Book of 1903, R. J. Mecredy attacked motoring's decriers, declared that cars promised a vast improvement in street hygiene, and felt that since motor buses occupied half the space and travelled at three times the speed of horse-drawn cabs 'in any given street with the same amount of passengers, the congestion will be reduced more than half.'

The prophecy, of course, remained unfulfilled. In 1914 there were still 11,000 horsedrawn cabs plying for hire in London, and the mixture of handcarts, barrows, motor buses, and cars was a chaotic one.

Each of the succession of measures instituted over the years had attempted to deal with a specific problem or aspect of a problem, rather than go to the root cause of traffic problems. Indeed, some measures themselves contributed to the cumulative confusion and congestion. It was not until the late 1950s that traffic engineering began to be recognised in Britain as a discipline in its own right.

The headlong development of car manufacture and ownership in the United States was the spur to many of the measures which came in after the First World War. Manually operated three-colour traffic signals were first installed in New York in 1918, with the first automatic lights in Detroit in 1919. Britain's first manually-operated lights (since the Westminster gas semaphore device) were tried out in London's Piccadilly in 1925 (they had two colours only), while the first British automatic traffic three-colour signals were installed in Wolverhampton in 1926. These were fixed-time lights—the first vehicle-actuated signals were installed

separate authorities which had hitherto been free to dig up London streets how and when they liked. One of the early police innovations was the roundabout—first trials of which were in Aldwych in 1925, and such was the success of it that it was very quickly installed elsewhere. Road marking, 'Stop' signs and white lines came in through the 1920s.

1930 was a significant year—it saw the end of the 20 mph maximum speed, and the registration of Britain's one-millionth vehicle. The 30 mph rule in a built-up area was introduced in 1935. Motorists and

Preston by-pass) until December 1958.

The 1950s at last saw Britain waking up to the deeper implications of heavy motor traffic and its effect on people. The first zebra pedestrian crossing was installed in October 1951, and a programme to reduce the large numbers of uncontrolled pedestrian crossings and make them all zebra-design was undertaken. Flashing beacons at the crossings were introduced in 1953. The first shots in what was to become the great parking war were fired—parking meters had been invented by an American, Carl Magee, and first used in Oklahoma in

lorry drivers, continuing the tradition of the AA scouts who had devised warning signals to warn of police stopwatch speed traps until an AA prosecution in 1909, created a new series of signals to warn of the new breed of police traffic patrols.

The police tried both extremes—both conspicious and disguised patrol vehicles. But in 1932, following complaints, the disguising of patrol cars and motor-cycle combinations (the last of these went in 1933) was discontinued. Today the police policy is to be as conspicuous as possible, this having proved to produce a better standard of behaviour in motorists than the fear of being caught. Also in 1932 it was decided to extend on-the-spot written cautions or verbal warnings to traffic offences. As a result, only 17 per cent of road incidents requiring police intervention were followed by prosecution, and the police became widely known as Courtesy Cops. This was hardly traffic manage-ment—but at the time, in the absence of the real thing, the police were as big an influence as anything else on traffic patterns and behaviour.

With traffic increasing, accidents rose too. Pedestrian crossings were introduced in 1934. Outside the towns, the old turnpike road system had been resurrected as the trunk road system, and its often devious routing was followed closely by local authorities without a thought for future volume needs. The then Lord Montague advocated a London–Liverpool motorway in 1924, and Germany's first autobahn was opened from Frankfurt to Darmstadt in 1935, yet Britain did not manage to build even its first traffic flyover (on the Winchester by-pass) until 1939, or the first real motorway (the

1935, but it was not until 1956 that the first British experiment—by Westminster City Council in a small part of Mayfair and Marylebone—was tried. Two years later meters came into full operation in London, and meters were soon sprouting in almost every large British town. New police powers were granted in 1957 to move cars causing an obstruction—they towed away 4000 in London in their first year—but the essentially punitive approach by the police underwent a change in 1959, when a new policy came in: accident prevention, the freer circulation of traffic, and the enforcement of traffic regulations in support of the other two. The traffic management aspects to which the police had instinctively been groping for so long were at last beginning to surface.

Britain's first traffic wardens set to work in Mayfair in 1960 with their shoulder-bags and little books of fixed-penalty parking tickets. In 1968 residents' park-ing schemes were introduced. In London, scene of most of the major experiments in traffic control and engineer-ing, police divisional traffic control was started in 1963, and a new approach to accidents was instituted with the formation of an accident research branch. In 1965 a road safety branch was set up. In the same year a major step forward came in motorway surveillance in Britain with the setting up of a control post at Hounslow police station to cover the M4 with the aid of closed-circuit television, a detector warning system, and an emer-gency motorway phone circuit. Central control later moved to a custom-built centre at Heston.

Police supervision of town traffic in Britain took a leap with the West London Traffic Control experiment

Above: an 'electric man' with a waving arm tells traffic that there is a blockage in the road. The 'man' does not get tired and can stand in mid stream without worry

Above right: as can be seen, our man can be transported all over his native America with few problems, and be ready to warn of road blockages and other traffic-stopping occurrences

in 1968, covering six square miles from Knightsbridge to Hammersmith Broadway, using a computer to phase traffic lights to aid flows through the area. A similar scheme was instituted in Glasgow, though this placed greater emphasis on flexibility, permitting experiments involving a wide range of control techniques. Neither scheme was able to show any marked advantage of a 'traffic-sensitive' control system as opposed to a 'fixed time' system, and accordingly the policies for wide-area control in cities throughout Britain were formulated around fixed-time control, but with the

Above: a London Transport Routemaster bus travels against the grain of one-way traffic in Piccadilly. He has to use his lights to warn pedestrians of his approach the 'wrong way.' Many lanes for buses in London are simply painted in the road with buses travelling with the traffic, but where it is thought that special roads will further ease congestion even more, they are constructed

flexibility afforded by several plans held in the computer, each there for selection according to the time of day or special circumstances.

London is in the process of extending its West London control. With subsequent modifications and greater sophistication, a big network of detectors buried in the streets to measure traffic flows—supplemented by TV cameras at particularly sensitive junctions—now feeds back constant information to an enlarged control room at New Scotland Yard.

The experience gained in London and Glasgow has enabled local authority proposals for wide-area traffic control to be dealt with intelligently and decisively. Leicester, Liverpool, Coventry, Nottingham and Northampton have all advanced schemes which have gained approval. Nottingham's is being instituted this autumn. Not that the policy-makers are totally satisfied with results to date—each of these schemes is the subject of intense study to see what more may be learned.

But while computers are steadily coming into use to keep wide-area traffic problems to a minimum, much remains in the hands of the local police—in an average year the Metropolitan Police issue 82,000 mobile signs and signals, and ease up to 17,000 abnormal loads through some of the world's busiest streets.

The fact that fairly rapid and sweeping changes have come about—and that capital expenditure has been available to make them possible—has been largely due to changed attitudes.

While traffic engineering was formally defined as early as 1924 in America, it was not until the late 1950s that it became a recognised and distinct science in Britain. The watershed came in November 1963 with the publication of the report 'Traffic in Towns' by Professor Colin Buchanan, which made six main points:

That the control of future traffic problems would depend entirely upon our ability to control the use of land; that the solution to existing traffic problems depended on the resolution of the conflict between accessibility and environment; that the answer to this conflict lay in the rationalisation of towns and cities into road networks and environmental areas; that the highway system achieving this would have to consist of a 'hierarchy' of custom-built road types, with for instance motorway-style through routes separating pedestrians and local traffic from fast traffic, and various sub-networks serving local purposes; that environment areas should be served by roads which could not subsequently be used to destroy that environment; and that restraint on traffic should be applied to non-essential journeys at peak times.

Through the late '60s a plethora of idealistic reports appeared to amplify some of Buchanan's basics—the separation of pedestrians and traffic in particular. A good deal of work was also done on schemes for rapid-transit systems whereby small automatic taxis running on track systems (usually overhead) might ferry commuters from dormitory to work areas. There was too a general renaissance in the belief that public transport could take over the function of the car in the city rush-hour, and the whole business became very closely linked in the public and political mind with the general acrimony being accorded the car over its constructional safety and the air pollution caused by vehicle exhaust.

A very positive ban-the-car lobby developed, with a strong body of opinion preferring to think in terms of preventing the environmental effects of the car rather than re-designing around saturation car-ownership. Again London has been in the forefront of the controversy, the 1973 GLC elections were fought around London's traffic problems, and at time of writing there are proposals to introduce supplementary licensing for owning a car in London, and for driving into London. Other possible systems aimed at cutting traffic density include variations on road pricing, and a programme of reducing London on-street parking spaces is already under way. Some 8000 parking meters have been removed.

These plans, environmentally understandable and praiseworthy but too single-minded to be strictly practical in a complex situation like London's, are under severe attack from motoring organisations, politicians in opposition, borough councils, and commercial, business and transportation groups. Several new and very active associations have been formed to fight restraint.

Quite apart from the assault on individual liberty and convenience which restraint implies, it is argued, the public transport system which is supposed to take the car-deprived travellers in their thousands could never cope. The London which is still managing to gasp on despite the strangulating effect of traffic jams would, say the anti-restraint lobby, die from the centre outwards if cars were as severely discouraged as the planners currently in office wish. Some evidence has been produced that the car commuter identified by the GLC as the villain is not in truth as numerous as has been suggested, and that restraint would hit the wrong sort of motorist. EF

Swift Swede

TOP SWEDISH RALLY DRIVER Tom Trana was born in Kristinehamm on 29 November 1937. Both his parents were keen motor-sport enthusiasts, his father competing on motorcycles and his mother with cars. In 1956, as soon as he was old enough to hold a licence, Trana purchased an old Volvo which he rebuilt for racing and rallying.

Trana won his class in many 1958 Swedish rallies and the following year he took second place in the Swedish Racing Championship to Volvo star Gunnar Andersson. In 1960 he conquered Andersson in the series and was given a car from Volvo with which he repeated his success in 1961 and 1962. He was also Swedish Ice Racing Champion in 1961 and Swedish Rally Champion in 1962.

His first trek outside Scandinavia was in 1962 when he entered the RAC Rally of Great Britain. He had been asked to drive a works Mini-Cooper S navigated by Ron Crellin and justified the faith put in him by BMC by setting best time on four special stages and being in the top three until a drive-shaft broke.

Volvo entered Tom in overseas events in 1963. He was seventh in the Tulip Rally and then returned to Great Britain to win the RAC Rally outright in a Volvo PV544 co-driven by Sven Lindström. The forest special stages suited the Scandinavians in general and Trana in particular. The following season was undoubtedly 26-year-old Trana's most successful, culminating with his being declared European Rally Champion. With Lindström he was sixth in the Monte Carlo Rally, but later with Gunnar Thermänius he enjoyed a string of successes: he won the Acropolis Rally and the Swedish Rally to the Midnight Sun, was second in Finland's Rally of the 1000 Lakes, sixth in the Geneva Rally and rounded up his year with a repeat win in the RAC Rally of Great Britain.

By contrast, Tom Trana's 1965 season was one to forget. He won the Swedish Rally, but in June's Gulf London Rally, a non-championship event which attracted a strong Scandinavian entry—including Trana and Gunnar Thermänius in a works Volvo B18 Amazon, which was making its competition *début*—tragedy intervened. A road crash before the second stage in Monmouthshire resulted in the death of Thermänius. Trana escaped from the wrecked car suffering from shock. Due to a pending dangerous driving charge, the Volvo team decided to withdraw from the end-of-season RAC Rally.

In 1966 Trana was Swedish Champion. He finished third in the Swedish Rally, fourth in the Group 2 section of the Tulip Rally, second in the Rally of the 1000 Lakes and third in the RAC Rally of Great Britain. His new co-driver was taxi driver Solvë Andreasson.

Volvo retired from motor sport, so Trana changed camps. He moved to Saab, but apart from a win in the Norwegian Rally he had a dismal year. Trana continued with Saab for the remainder of his rallying days, also carrying out much of their test and development driving. He competed in fewer rallies until his virtual retirement in the early 1970s when he concentrated on administration. Like Timo Mäkinen and other top Scandinavians he developed an interest in power boat racing.

In 1968 Trana won his class in Swedish Rally Championship: he was second in the Swedish and Norwegian rallies and ninth in the Austrian Alpine, but played no part in Saab's 1–2 triumph in the RAC Rally of Great Britain as he was an early retirement. In 1969 he was third in the Norwegian Rally and seventh in both the Swedish Rally and the RAC Rally of Great Britain. In 1970 he was fourth in the San Remo-Sestriere Rally in Italy and the following year saw his last placing in a major event: he finished 10th in the Swedish Rally.   MK

Tom Trana, *below*, seen in action in the car that he rallied in the later years of his career, the Saab 96

TRANA

POWER TO THE WHEELS

The duty of the transmission train is to transfer the power produced by the engine to the driving wheels

Below: a longitudinal section through a Fiat 1400 of 1950; this had a conventional layout, with the engine at the front and propeller-shaft drive to the rear wheels; the prop-shaft is split in the centre, and has a mounting there

SOME OF THE VERY EARLIEST MOTOR VEHICLES, things like Edward Butler's 1885 tricycle, had virtually no transmission system, the driving wheel spindle constituting a crankshaft to which the pistons were linked by long connecting rods in an emulation of steam locomotive practice. They were horrible. Car designers soon learned that the inability of the internal combustion engine to furnish controllable torque from zero rpm made some sort of complex transmission system essential. That is equally horrible. There have been efforts aplenty to substitute some other kind of motive power unit, but all the proposed alternatives to the internal combustion engine have shown even greater drawbacks. The transmission system, in all its variety of component detail between the engine crankshaft and the driving wheels of the car, therefore emerges as the least of necessary evils, a burden less troublesome than any feasible alternative.

Every modern car has a transmission system incorporating at least four component sub-assemblies, but the number can rise to seven: a clutch, a gearbox, an overdrive, a propeller shaft, the final drive or 'axle' gearing, the differential gearing, and the half-shafts finally transmitting torque to the driving wheels. They do not always appear in that order: sometimes the propeller shaft comes first in the drive line, sometimes it lies between the clutch and gearbox, sometimes it does not seem to be there at all but can be traced in vestigial form as a quill shaft passing through the transmission aggregate of a mid-engined or rear-engined car; sometimes the necessary differential action is provided by the gearbox or whatever takes its place, as in early versions of the Daf Variomatic Transmission.

It is normal and fairly logical for the first item in the drive-line to be the clutch. Its function is to permit progressive engagement and disengagement of the

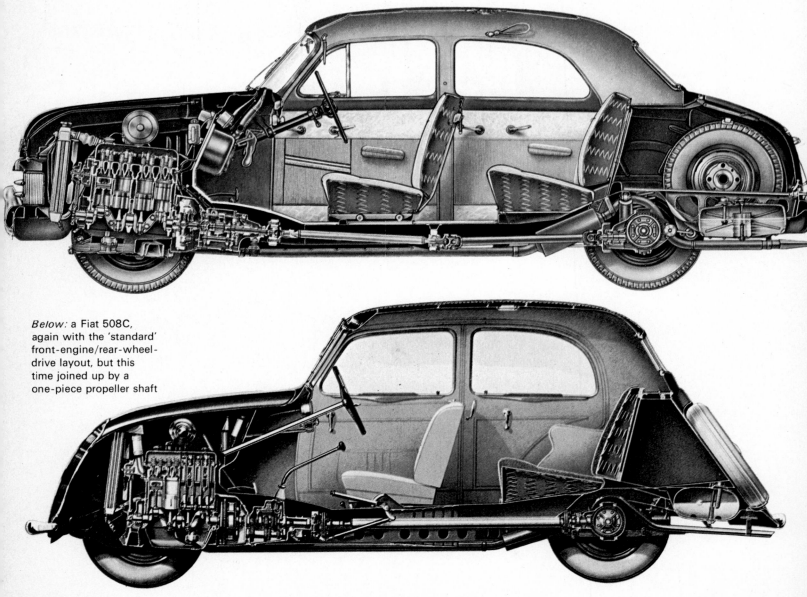

Below: a Fiat 508C, again with the 'standard' front-engine/rear-wheel-drive layout, but this time joined up by a one-piece propeller shaft

Left: a cutaway view of a diaphragm-spring clutch, as used in the majority of modern cars

Below: the transmission system of the Series 1a Jeep, with four-wheel drive and the option of high or low ratios, giving six speeds from the three-speed gearbox

Bottom: the Variomatic transmission system, with its variable-diameter pulleys and belts, is unique in the DAF range and had been used on every DAF car up to the time that Volvo took over; it gives smooth, stepless ratio-changes

action resulted in either uncomfortably long pedal travel and troublesome adjustment problems, or the fierceness of the cone clutch which was generally abandoned in the late 1920s. By the end of that decade the Föttinger fluid coupling was being tried, notably by Daimler in Britain, in an attempt to ensure perfectly progressive take-up of the drive and to relieve the driver of the need for skill at the pedal. This was a success when combined with epicyclic gearboxes of the Wilson type, and led in due course to the modern automatic transmission which usually embodies a more sophisticated fluid coupling with a third element allowing it to multiply the torque in certain circumstances, reducing the number of gears or gearchanges necessary, but so far never efficient enough to be relied on entirely to the exclusion of some form of variable-ratio gearbox or its equivalent.

The clutch may be crude, but it was the gearbox that was the *bête noire* of early drivers and remains so for some. There have been countless variations on the simple two-shaft gearbox that the great French pioneers Panhard and Renault popularised in the 1890s. The number of ratios offered has varied from two to eight, according to the torque characteristics of the engine, the weight of the vehicle, and the performance expected of it. Sometimes one of the ratios has by-passed the secondary or lay shaft to provide a direct

engine from the rest of the drive-line, the principle requirement being ease of moving the car away from rest with the engine running, and a secondary consideration being ease of gear-changing (which does not need clutch disengagement for some modern types of transmissions, and did not need it with some of the older kinds if the driver were sufficiently skilled). In its conventional simple form, the clutch is probably the crudest piece of machinery in the car, an engine-driven disc being controllably clamped to another so that friction and clamping forces will combine to make them rotate as one. The slower it turns, the larger it needs to be in order to transmit a given power; the larger its diameter, the more power it can manage at a given speed, but the more highly stressed it will be mechanically. Also, the greater the difference between the outer and inner diameters of the friction surfaces, the greater the difference in rubbing velocities when the clutch is deliberately slipped in controlled engagement, and therefore the greater the risk will be of local overheating or other damage.

Most of these problems can be resolved if necessary by multiplying the number of clutch plates and reducing their diameters. Clutches of the multi-plate type take up the drive very smoothly, but do not always disengage as cleanly as they should, which was why double declutching was unnecessary when changing down in a Bugatti. The multi-plate clutch of the Bugatti was unusual on two other counts, first in being lubricated by partial immersion in a mixture of oil and paraffin, and also in being reliant on a system of weights and levers to increase the clamping force as engine rpm increased, the centrifugal loads being adjustable so that the clutch could be made very fierce or docile and sensitive. Wet or oil-immersed clutches were popular in the late 1930s, and centrifugal assistance has often been contrived, notably in the so-called 'traffic' clutch of pre-war Rileys fitted with Wilson pre-selector gearboxes, and more recently in the Daf transmission which is steplessly variable between fairly wide limits and only needs a clutch for starting and stopping. Centrifugal assistance can act simply as a servo, making the pedal action lighter in low-speed driving; all other attempts to contrive adequate clamping forces with light pedal

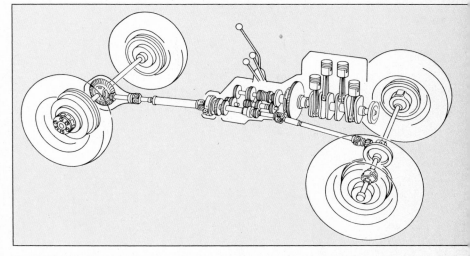

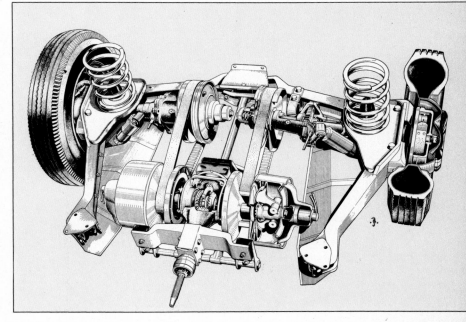

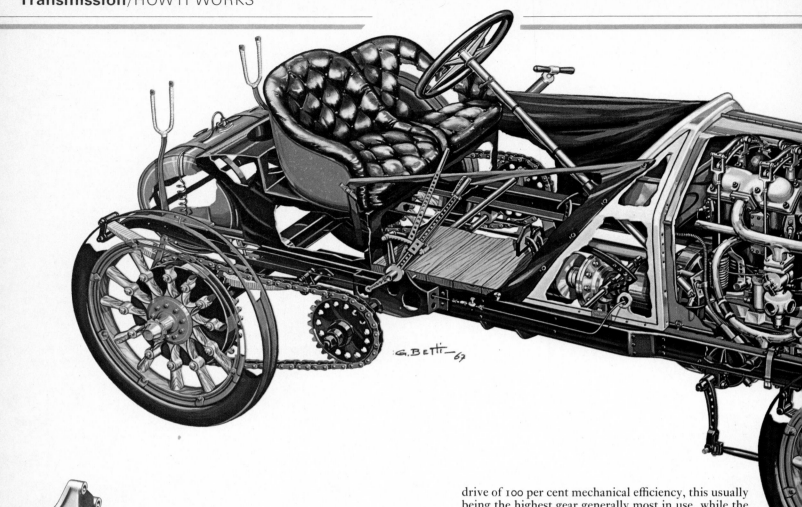

G.Betti '67

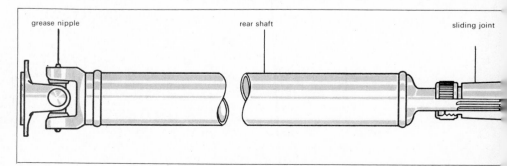

drive of 100 per cent mechanical efficiency, this usually being the highest gear generally most in use, while the other ratios would iinvolve at least two pairs of meshing gears, bringing the efficiency down to 96 per cent or less. Sometimes all the gears are indirect, each involving one step down through a pair of meshing gears; mechanical efficiency is approximately the same in all ratios. The indirect gears of early boxes involved sliding pinions into engagement, but constant-mesh gears clamped to their shafts by axially engaged teeth (dog-clutches) proved easier to manage, and allowed the gears to be formed with helical teeth instead of straight ones, mechanical efficiency being sacrificed to quietness. From this it was a short step to the modern synchromesh gearbox, in which miniature clutches equalise the speeds of rotation of the dogs before they engage. Until synchromesh became universal in manually-operated gearboxes, some skill was still needed; and many engineers were attracted by the possibilities of epicyclic or planetary gear trains that were in constant mesh and could be controlled by friction clutches acting on the outside of the internally toothed annulus gears or on the armatures that carried the planetary pinions.

Not everybody liked the idea of gears. Some pre-

Above: an automatic gearbox from the ZF company of Germany; these units have been used by a great many of the world's car manufacturers. A torque convertor takes the place of the clutch and epicyclic gear clusters are used to provide the various ratios

Right: a two-piece propellershaft, with three universal joints—two of the Hooke type and one of the rubber-doughnut variety—and a central bearing; sliding splines are employed between the two parts, in order to allow changes in length

grease nipple   rear shaft   sliding joint

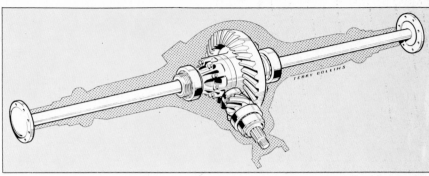

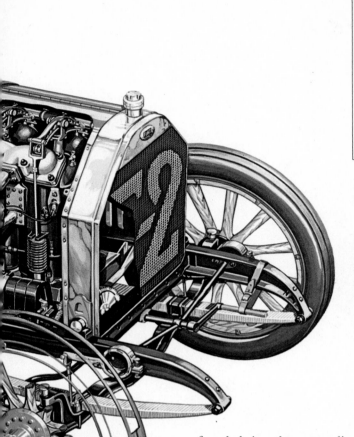

Above: a heavy-duty final-drive unit from a Ford truck of the 1970s

Left: a cutaway of the 1907 Fiat Grand Prix car, with shaft drive from its front engine, through the gearbox, to a transverse shaft, and thence by chain to the rear wheels

ferred chains, the outstanding example being the GN transmission in which the two-shaft layout of an all-indirect gearbox was emulated on a larger scale by a counter-shaft carrying sprockets linked by chains to corresponding sprockets on the solid rear axle. There was no differential, and the bevel gears that were needed to turn the drive through a right angle from the propeller shaft were upstream of the stepped-ratio transmission, on the counter-shaft which carried dog-clutches to engage the chosen driving sprocket. It was a very pleasant, fast and easy gearchange, and it survived in Frazer-Nash cars until 1940, but it was neither clean nor reliable, and the absence of a differential made it suitable only for outright sports cars. Chain drive had been in widespread use up to 1911, but only as a final drive from a counter-shaft to independent sprockets on the rear wheels—a conventional clutch, gearbox, propeller shaft, and bevel gear with differential, completing the drive line between the engine and the counter-shaft. It was a nice system in its elimination of torque effects on the rear suspension, and in its minimisation of unsprung weight; but it was noisy, dirty and space-consuming.

Others preferred belts. Many of the early light cars and cyclecars got along well enough with a system of fast and loose pulleys or expanding pulleys to give a choice of speeds. The Variomatic, invented in Holland by Hubertus van Doorne, in which expanding and contracting pulleys are controlled not only by applied engine torque but also by inlet manifold vacuum, with override controls switched by the brake and accelerator pedals, probably comes closest to being the ideal transmission, but is still limited in its applications by the inability of belts to transmit the power of large engines. All other transmission systems, despite the interpolation of fluid couplings in some cases, depend on a number of discrete ratios, commonly 3, 4 or 5, and these have to be determined with some care to satisfy the requirements of hill starting, traffic driving, acceleration, easy cruising, maximum speed, and—most importantly—cost accounting. The lowest ratio must be low enough to permit starting on the steepest gradient likely to be encountered, but there is no point in making it so low that the multiplication of torque results in a greater tractive effort than the tyres can transmit without spinning on the road surface. The highest ratio may be calculated for the car to reach the greatest speed of which it is theoretically capable, or to prevent the engine from overspeeding at any speed the car is likely to achieve, or it may be made deliberately low for the sake of easy top-gear performance or a reduction in the number of intermediate ratios.

The opportunities for sustained high speed presented by the new motorways of Europe, and the limitations of existing gearboxes, combined to prompt the development of overdrive devices which could supplement an existing gearbox to give an extra high ratio. This became a British speciality in the 1950s, and the Laycock de Normanville overdrive proved to be an exceptionally refined and easily controlled but heavy and expensive adjunct to existing transmission designs. Hopes that it might lead to some kind of partial automaticity were not realised, however, and the overdrive is now fighting a losing rearguard battle against modern synchromesh gearboxes with five speeds instead of four.

Between the gearbox (and the overdrive if any) and the final drive or axle gearing, there is in the majority of front-engined rear-driven cars a propeller shaft, familiarly known as the prop-shaft and once dignified by the name of its inventor, Cardan. In essentials it is a simple tubular shaft (a solid one would be heavier and too likely to bend) incorporating some form of universal joint at each end, permitting relative movement between the gearbox—which usually rocks with the engine on flexible bearers—and the rear axle, which may move up and down on its springs. If the rear suspension is independent, the final drive gears will be housed in a case fixed to the chassis, and relative movement will be comparatively slight, but must still be allowed for. The movement of a live axle is much more demanding, for the angular displacement of the shaft is accompanied by a variation in the distance between its extremities, and

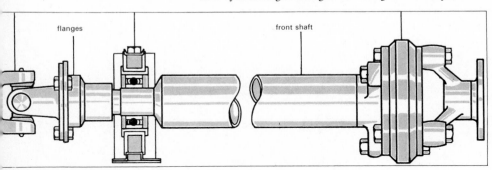

flanges

front shaft

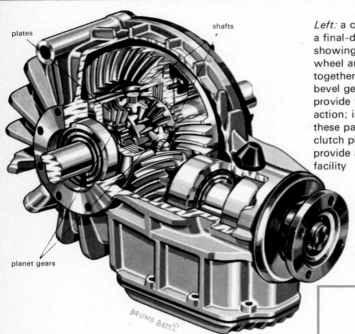

plates

shafts

planet gears

BRUNO BELL

Left: a cutaway view of a final-drive unit, showing the crown wheel and pinion, together with the small bevel gears used to provide the differential action; in addition to these parts, the unit has clutch plates built in to provide a 'limited-slip' facility

effective in performance, usually consisting of two inward-facing bevel sun gears linked by a cluster of two or more bevel planetaries, although spur-gear differentials have been extensively used in the past, as in the Austin 7. Cars with more power than traction or suspension control often need a self-locking differential to avoid the inconvenience resulting from excessive wheelspin, and if it is thought necessary this can be embodied in one of its three currently popular forms, all of which rely upon friction to make the differential deliberately inefficient.

That leaves the half-shafts, which finally communicate torque to the hubs of the driving wheels. If those wheels are independently suspended, the half-shafts will be beset by the same problems of articulation as the prop-shaft of a live-axle car, with the design of the universal joints complicated in the case of front-wheel-drive cars by the need for the wheels to be turned for steering. If the half-shafts are enclosed in a live rear axle, they are simple enough, but care still has to be

some form of telescoping joint is necessary to provide for this. A splined slip joint is usual, but the splines tend to bind when subjected to really high torque, and high-powered cars sometimes have to have a more expensive form of slip joint in which ball bearings are interposed.

A drive shaft with a universal joint at only one end creates problems of variable angular velocity of rotation. One with universals at both ends creates problems of whirl, and it may also be difficult to balance. A common counter-measure is to make the prop-shaft in two parts, with the central joint (another universal) supported by a flexibly mounted steady bearing. Another way out of the difficulty would be to put the gearbox at the mid-point, as is done in the Morgan, but the space it occupies is seldom to be spared. Cars with independent rear suspension are sometimes arranged with the gearbox at the rear, perhaps in unit with the final-drive casing, in the interests of mass distribution: this creates its own problems, for the rotational inertia of the prop-shaft is added to that of all the other rotating portions of the gearbox and clutch that have to be slowed or accelerated by the synchromesh mechanism during gearchanging.

In any case the prop-shaft is a confounded nuisance, and several of the arguments in favour of front-wheel-drive or rear engine location turn on its elimination. If in either of these cases the engine be set with its crankshaft athwart, the final reduction gearing from the gearbox output shaft to the axle shafts can be by cylindrical gears, either straight-cut or of helical tooth formation. Otherwise the drive line would have to be turned through 90° by bevel or worm gearing, which is more expensive to produce and less easy to accommodate. The choice of gearing may be determined by the displacement (if any) between the axes of the input and output shafts: if there is no displacement the bevel gears may be straight-toothed for efficiency or of spiral form for quietness, if there is a slight displacement the hypoid bevel will be necessary, and if it is larger then the designer must resort to worm gearing, which sometimes creates problems in lubrication. Whatever the type of final drive gearing, it must—or should, *pace* Frazer-Nash enthusiasts—incorporate differential gearing to permit the inner and outer wheels to be driven at different speeds when cornering. Differential gearing is surprisingly simple in construction, and normally

Above: the front-wheel-drive layout of the Audi 100, with a transaxle unit taking the drive from the engine to the front wheels; the disc brakes are fitted on the inboard end of the drive shafts, to reduce unsprung weight

taken in their design because the torque they transmit is greater than that passed by any other component in the transmission system. Every gear reduction produces torque multiplication, and by the time that the rotation of the engine's crankshaft has been reduced through a bottom gear which may be as low as 4:1 and again through the final-drive gearing which may be of similar magnitude, the half-shaft will be turning at a sixteenth or less of the rate of the crankshaft. Even allowing for all the mechanical losses on the way, the multiplication of torque will be of a similar order—and although a conventional differential will divide that torque equally between the two half-shafts, a self-locking one may act to pass all or most of it through one whenever the tyre on the other loses its grip. It is little wonder that a broken half-shaft was for a long time the most common transmission failure, and continues frequently to affect racing cars. There are still designers who dream of alternative systems that will get rid of all these difficulties, of hydraulic pumps driven by the engine supplying hydraulic motors in the wheel hubs, of electric drives, and so on; but in fact the transmission system of the typical modern motorcar has changed less in the past 70 years than any other major sub-assembly. Perhaps this means that it is a lot better than we generally give it credit for—but the substantial power losses commonly accounted for in the transmission system give us cause to doubt it.　　　LJKS

CHEAP THRILLS & DIRTY WEEKENDS

Cheap and enjoyable, sporting trials are a welcome breath of fresh air to the world of motor sport

IN THESE DAYS of exorbitantly escalating costs, sporting trials are a pleasing anomaly: a last bastion of the cheap, truly amateur, purely fun type of sport surviving from the simpler years of the '20s, '30s and '50s. Spartan, two-seater sporting trials cars can still be built for as little as £150 and a day's sport had for a gallon of petrol.

In the early 1920s bands of enthusiasts found there was splendid fun to be had from pitting their ordinary road cars against muddy hills, mastering the conditions to climb to the top without stopping en route. The sport caught on to such an extent that it even attracted manufacturers' participation before World War II. MG, for example, produced special versions of their current sports cars for the famous Cream Cracker and Musketeers trials teams.

With cars and fuel hard to come by in the postwar years, trials were a godsend to motoring enthusiasts. All sorts of production sports cars and specials—particularly Ford V8s—were pressed into action. Just such an enthusiast was young Colin Chapman, who constructed his very first Lotus, an Austin Seven Special, for trials in 1947. MGs remained popular, of course, and in the early '50s mud-stained specialist sports cars such as Allards were a common sight on the hills.

As the events became more difficult, so ordinary sports cars became less suited to the tests and specialised trial cars began to rule the roost. One such was the Dellow, a side-valve Ford-engined, two-seater, road-trimmed sports car of short wheelbase, remarkable agility and exceptional traction. Gradually trials specials became smaller, lighter—and cruder—evolving into the sporting trials cars as we know them today. They became so popular in the early '50s that a

whole new sport with separate regulations was created for them. Sporting trials had arrived and production-car trials went their separate way.

Mud has always been regarded as a prerequisite of sporting trials, which accounts for it having developed as a rainy-season sport usually crammed into a period beginning in October and running through to the end of April, or early May.

Most trials are run on Sundays and provide competitors with a day packed full of competitive motoring, beginning at about 9 AM and carrying through till darkness with just a brief break for lunch. During this hectic day each competitor will tackle anything from 24 to 36 hills—well, usually 12 hills or so covered several times. Most trials are run in wooded countryside, taking advantage of natural obstacles such as trees, rocks and streams to make the hills—or 'sections', as they're called—more difficult. Each eight or nine-foot-wide section is marked off with poles numbered in descending order from 12 to one from the bottom of the hill.

Below: 'Am I going to make it?' wonders the driver of this trials car as he attempts to pilot his machine through a particularly tight corner. His passenger is attempting to assert some influence on the direction of travel by leaning out of the car as far as possible

There's no flinging the car at the hill from a flying start: the car must be at a standstill, though to give everybody a fighting chance, most start lines are sited on level ground. From there the driver and his mandatory passenger ('bouncer' in trials jargon) must maintain unassisted forward motion to the top of the hill. If they stop they fail, whether or not they manage to restart; penalty marks are awarded according to the number on the nearest marker post. If the car reaches the top, which means having all four wheels past the final marker post, no penalty points are awarded, which means that the winner at the end of the day is the driver with the least number of penalty points. However, not only must he maintain that all-important forward motion up the hill, he must also keep the car within the indicated width and avoid hitting the marker posts, or pay the cost of the penalty marks written on the appropriate post.

Despite the sport's rapidly increasing popularity in Britain there are only about 200 trials cars in the country, a surprisingly low figure which has been dictated not by lack of demand but by lack of supply. There simply are not enough cars made to go round. In point of fact this position is gradually improving, but the fact remains that if you own a decent trials car you are likely to be able to sell it for more than you paid. Entries for individual events vary from 25 to 50.

There are three classes for trials cars, of which the most popular is the National Formula. At present this class has no capacity restrictions, leading to the arrival on the scene of a few 2-litre engined cars, which has caused a certain amount of soul-searching and the decision to institute a 1650 cc maximum restriction for 1976. Trials are particularly safe, injuries being practically non-existent, but a surfeit of power applied at the wrong time, for instance on a 1 in 2 gradient, would instantly whip the car over backwards with obvious risks to its occupants, so this is what the new regulation is intended to avoid.

Right at the bottom of the trials car formulae is the 750 cc class, events for which are run, appropriately enough, by the 750 Motor Club. Originally the pre-war, side-valve Austin Seven engine provided the motive power, or lack of it; though several such engined devices survive, the 750 cc overhead-valve Reliant unit has generally replaced that old faithful, just as it has in the Club's cheap 750 circuit racing formula. If cheap motoring sport is the object, then there can be little cheaper than trials with a 750 car—anybody with the necessary talents should find it possible to build himself a car for as little as £150.

Next up the scale is the 950 cc class, likewise organised by the 750 Motor Club. This too is an exceptionally cheap formula, with the power unit restricted to untuned 948 cc BMC A-series engines, ex-Morris Minor or A35. An ideal starting point for the novice driver, this class keeps the National Formula refreshed with new blood.

Above left: Stirling Moss and his attractive lady passenger competing in a sporting trial. Moss, in spite of his considerable driving talent, took quite some time to assimilate the totally different skills required for trials driving

Top right: the sparse cockpit of a trials machine owned by a member of the 750 Motor Club. Note the twin 'fiddle brake' levers

Above: some idea of the stark simplicity of a trials car can be gauged from this picture of Gordon Jackson's Ford Mexico-engined Ibex

Above: right at the bottom of the trials-car formulae is the 750 cc class, events for which are run by the 750 Motor Club. Originally, the pre-war, side-valve Austin Seven engine provided the power, but this has now been replaced by the 750 cc overhead-valve Reliant motor. Next up the scale is the 950 cc class and this is also organised by the 750 Motor Club. In this class, the predominant power units are untuned 948 cc BMC A-series engines, ex-Morris Minor or Austin A35

Of the several trials championships run in Britain the most important is the Semperit-BTRDA (British Trials and Rally Drivers' Association) series. This consists of 25 rounds spread throughout England and scored on a points system. The top 25 competitors at the end of the series qualify for the British Experts Gold Star run-off final to decide the Champion. Trials can turn up some unexpected results and the '75 final was no exception in that the Gold Star, the premier trials award, went to Laurie Brown in his Aberties car, who vanquished all the established stars. The next 25 drivers in the BTRDA series qualify for the Silver Star (formerly the British Junior) run-off. Within the BTRDA series, the Royal Automobile Club runs the National Trials Championship, based on a points system from selected BTRDA events.

Another Championship which is rapidly gaining in popularity and status is the Duckhams South–East series, run on a points system, the best six results from the right events to count. The cost of tow-car petrol for trailing trials cars long distances to events, coupled with onerous speed restrictions, is undoubtedly aiding the success of this convenient, localised series. Yet when Duckhams Oils tried to organise a similar series in the North, it failed to get off the ground. The 1975 Duckhams award went to the very competent Gordon Jackson, once a 'works' AJS motor-cycle trials rider—one of the best in the world in fact and holder of the best-ever result in the International Scottish Six Days'

motor-cycle trial. Gordon's wife Peggy did the bouncing in the Ibex car designed and constructed by her husband.

All these purpose-built cars from whichever class are constructed on similar lines: a front engine mounted well back behind the front axle line to push the weight towards the rear tyres for better traction, a tubular-steel, space-frame chassis panelled in aluminium or glass fibre and a live rear axle suspended on coil springs (although there is nothing to stop the use of independent rear suspension—just that a live axle seems to work best). Front beam axles are predominant along with rack and pinion steering. The cockpit is a sparse, cramped affair with just sufficient room for the bouncer to jump around in his—or her—well-padded seat to increase traction. There are no weight restrictions and most cars weigh about 8 cwt.

While it might be possible to build a 750 class car for £150 or buy an old 1172 cc, side-valve Ford-engined car, once the King of Trials, for a similar amount, it is equally possible if you're a friend of Jack Pearce, expert trials driver and Midlands engineer, to spend £2–3000 on one of the two or three Kincraft trials cars he produces each year as special favours. Not that this would be a guarantee of success, for skill is a great leveller and much more vital than sophisticated machinery in the trials world and Jack himself often loses out to cheaper cars—but not often enough to prevent him becoming RAC Trials Champion of '75. And to have

Above: the most prolific make of trials car available in 1975 was the Cannon. These were built by Mike Cannon who has the distinction of an entry in the Guinness Book of Records as the smallest one-man operation manufacturing motorcars. Here a Cannon vehicle is seen in action

adaptations are kept secret by their instigators, but one such example is the Hillman clutch incorporated in the 1275 cc A-series Cannon car of Colin Taylor, one of the leading drivers.

Mark 1 Cortina gearboxes predominate in trials cars, though Jack Pearce's Renault 16-engined Kincraft features a special two-speed Hewland gearbox. Rear axles need to be especially robust, the Ford Anglia axle with the added attribute of large drum brakes being almost universal. Limited-slip differentials are banned and a 5.3:1 final drive ratio (a usefully available optional low ratio for the Ford axle) is most common.

No description of trials cars would be complete without mention of those beautifully named devices, 'fiddle' brakes. Each independent rear brake is connected to a separate hand lever, usually fitted on the outside of the car. In the old days Bowden cables were the operating medium, nowadays most cars employ hydraulic systems with a separate master cylinder to each brake. The idea of fiddle brakes is that when one

the Rolls-Royce of trials cars must be a great boost to confidence and ego. About £500 is the rock-bottom price one can expect to pay for a competitive entry in National Formula events.

Torque rather than power is the main criterion for a suitable engine in the National Formula, though power can still make the difference between winning or not if used in expert hands: extra power can burn the rear tyres through the mud to find grip where a smaller-engined car might grind to a halt. Favourite engines in current trials cars are the Ford 1600 cross-flow, the Renault 16 (all-aluminium, so very light) and the 1275 cc British Leyland A-series engine. There are also a couple of overhead-camshaft 1500 cc Moskvich engines in use, and 1098 cc A-series units abound. Most engines are fed by twin or single SU carburetters because of their good performance at steep angles and good throttle control. For example Gordon Jackson's Ford 1600GT engine in the Ibex dismisses its twin-choke Weber carburettor, which has too little progression between the chokes for this sort of application, in favour of a single SU. Some of the Renault engines employ Fish carburettors.

There have been interesting alternatives to the common recipes described above. A Coventry-Climax-engined car made an appearance in the days when the Ford 1172 engine was on top, but its power band proved unsuited to the big 18 in wheels and knobbly tyres employed in those days. Currently the Fack twins are running a 1000 cc Imp unit in National Formula events, an engine which demands about £600 to modify it and a lightweight crew to drive it.

Clutches take a caning in trials work, deliberate slipping often being essential. In most cases the standard clutch appropriate to the engine would be inadequate and much intelligent machining occurs to mate larger clutches into the drive line. Mostly these

wheel starts spinning because of the conventional differential it can be slowed by its individual brake to give it chance to regain traction in much the same way as a limited-slip differential would work. Much of the art of trials driving is based around these brakes which, used judiciously, enable the rear end of the car to be slewed round tight corners, the inside wheel being slowed whilst the outside continues to push. The front brakes are more of an afterthought—in case you actually need to stop the car—operated, often through Bowden cables, by the footbrake.

Another design feature which can be used to advantage by a clever driver is the tree bar, an angled, tough steel guard on each side of the car intended to prevent trees wedging themselves between the wheel and the bodywork. By leaning a tree bar against a handily-placed tree on a tight corner, a good driver can slew the car straight round without running out of steering lock.

Rear tyres are directly responsible for the all important grip. Until a couple of years ago, knobbly winter tyres were standard wear in all classes, but then regulations were changed to make ordinary road tyres

Right: the passenger in a trials car can play an extremely important part in achieving a 'clean run'. He (or she) helps to keep balance and, by adjusting his/her weight, assists to maintain traction. Anyone over sixteen can be a passenger, or bouncer; no competition licence is necessary for this exacting task, just flesh oblivious to bruises and reasonably agile limbs

Above: perhaps the most sophisticated trials cars produced are those built by Midlands engineer, Jack Pearce. Known as Kincrafts these machines can cost in the region of £2000 to £3000. This, however, is the exception to the rule as most trials machines can be built or bought for considerably less. In fact, it is possible to build a trials car for as little as £150

mandatory in the National Formula. Many competitors were up in arms about what they thought would be a retrograde step, foreseeing the end of trials as they knew it on knobbly tyres. In fact the opposite happened, the reduced grip of the road tyres putting more premium on driver skills and indeed developing new skills. The road tyres have been found to give more control, too, not gripping so suddenly and unexpectedly as knobblies were wont to do. Out of this regulation one tyre has emerged as King, the Semperit M401 steel-

construction radial, which provides phenomenal grip and has become standard wear for 95 per cent of National competitors. Semperit have almost captured the market in 750 and 950 formulas, too, in which knobbly tyres are allowed still, their M and S winter tyre being the most-used type. In the old days 18 in diameter rear wheels were fitted, but as tyres of this size became more and more difficult to obtain, the regulations were changed to allow 15 in wheels. Now all rear tyres are of 165×15 in size on $4\frac{1}{2}$ lb/sq in in the fight for grip, which entails the use of four security bolts to prevent the tyre rolling off the rim.

Front wheels are of secondary importance, the size and type of tyre being less critical. Narrow, wire wheels of 17 in to 19 in diameter shod with 3.50 section motor-cycle tyres are fitted.

To enter sporting trials, the essentials besides the trials car are an RAC Restricted Rally Licence available from the RAC Motor Sport Division, a tow car and a two-wheeled trailer. Anybody over the age of 16 can be a bouncer; no competition licence is required for this exacting occupation, just flesh oblivious to bruises and reasonably agile limbs. It also helps if driver and bouncer are of fairly equal weight. Actually, 'bouncer' is a misnomer, for bouncing up and down in the seat is no longer regarded as the way to increase traction, rather a side-to-side swaying motion, with weight spread as far back over the wheels as possible. Indeed some competitors with modern trials cars prefer to have their passengers sitting still, merely as lumps of ballast. The bouncer must also learn to transfer his or her weight with the direction of the slope, ie pointing up hill, if the car is sideways on a banking, to combat the urge for the car to turn turtle.

If the intending competitor plans to build his own car, he should make sure he watches several sporting trials first to see for himself exactly what the require-

ments and best features are. He must also build the car to comply with the RAC Trials Car Regulations, copies of which are available from the RAC Motor Sport Division. Alternatively he might look for a cheap, old trials car, probably a Cannon, the most prolific make in trials. Mike Cannon helped create the sporting trials formula when he set out to make his own cars over 20 years ago. One of his many claims to fame is an entry in the Guinness Book of Records as the smallest manufacturer of cars for a one-man business. In recent years he has been concentrating on the manufacture of trailers, but with increasing demand for trials cars his Kent farm is once again reverberating to the noise of car construction, with a new design on the way for 1976.

There can be few sports quite so friendly as sporting trials, the whole atmosphere being wonderfully sociable. The format lends itself to allowing competitors to make events a family day out—and lots of wives act as bouncers in any case. It's a healthy sport, too, with continuous exposure to fresh air and the reconnoitring walks up every hill doing wonders in the fight for healthy lungs and against flab. Of course, good waterproof clothing and boots are an essential part of any trials teams' equipment.

If you visit a sporting trial, don't bamboozle yourself into thinking that it's an easy form of competition. It may look easy, but in reality perfection is extraordinarily difficult to achieve: it's a whole new world demanding exceptional skills in throttle control, assessment of surfaces and gradients, intelligent use of fiddle brakes and the shrewd utilisation of natural obstacles to assist steering round what would normally be impossibly tight bends. Perhaps it is slow, all the sections being tackled in first, or at best second, gear, but some of those 1 in 2 gradients can be as daunting as a corner taken on a racing circuit at 130 mph. If you don't believe it, then ask Stirling Moss, who reckons that until he took up sporting trials he had not had so much enjoyment since his Grand Prix racing days. From an A-series-engined Cannon borrowed from Colin Taylor, Moss has progressed to a 2-litre Ford-engined Cannon and hopes to buy a new Ibex. Even this brilliant driver is taking time to assimilate those totally different skills of trials. Yet another escapee from single seaters is Embassy Hill Formula One driver Tony Brise, whose favourite relaxation is sporting trials driving behind the wheel of his Renault-engined Cannon. CR

A CONSTANT BATTLE FOR SURVIVAL

The history of the Trident company is the saga of a small manufacturer's long and difficult struggle against overwhelming odds

THE ORIGINS OF TRIDENT cars are bound up in financial problems that hit the Blackpool specialist car firms of TVR, which handled sales of TVR cars, and Grantura Engineering, which constructed them. TVR, producing a number of well liked coupé models, ran into cash-flow difficulties in 1965, and was unable to proceed with a new aluminium bodied fixed-head car design by Trevor Fiore. Two prototypes had already been constructed by Italian coachbuilder Fissore and attracted a good deal of attention at the 1965 Geneva Motor Show. The design was bought by a TVR agent, W. J. Last, of Woodbridge, Suffolk.

Last, who had a stake in Grantura, also persuaded the directors to authorise Fissore to undertake another prototype—a steel-bodied convertible based on an Austin-Healey chassis. Last went to Italy to collect this car, and returned to find that Grantura and TVR had gone into liquidation (though TVR was soon to be resuscitated on a sounder footing).

A new firm, Trident Cars Ltd, was established at Woodbridge with the very shapely convertible as its first model. The prototype appeared at the 1966 London Racing Car Show on the new company's stand. It was fitted with a 289 Ford 4727 cc V8 engine in a cruciform-based boxed-platform chassis with coil front and conventional semi-elliptic rear suspension. Fiore was called in again to design a 2 + 2 glassfibre fastback coupe on the Austin-Healey chassis, and it was this car, shown at the Racing Car Show of 1967, which began manufacture at a plant in Market Harborough, with a production goal of three cars weekly.

The Austin-Healey was discontinued shortly afterwards by British Motor Holdings, but Bill Last had duplicate chassis made, and the Trident was sold in kit form for £1923. Formidable acceleration (0–60 mph in 5.0 seconds), 150 mph top speed, 11-inch disc brakes all round, and very full interior specification including reclining seats and tinted glass made it attractive to the comparatively wealthy enthusiast. Coil and wishbone front suspension and a live rear axle located by torque arms and a Panhard rod gave good though rather heavy handling.

Much of the production was exported to the United States, but the knowledgeable on both sides of the Atlantic recognised the Trident as among the most impressive of the small 'muscle' road machines then available. The three-litre Ford V6 popular in so many British 'specials' was offered as an alternative in 1967, as well as open and closed bodywork.

In the latter part of 1968 production moved to Woodbridge, and the finish, which had been criticised, received special attention. By the time of the 1969 Racing Car Show the Trident had really taken on the look of a thoughtfully produced, well sorted and well finished challenger to better known cars of the type. A Trident V8 established a quarter-mile standing-start record of 14.3 seconds for GT cars under 5 litres at Santa Pod.

In 1969 production moved yet again, this time to Ipswich, and new versions of the car were shown at Earls Court. They utilised a TR6 floorpan lengthened by $5\frac{1}{2}$ inches. The V8 was named the Clipper, and the V6 was dubbed Venturer.

In the course of 1970 there were modifications to the bodywork including slight lengthening and an improvement in the rear headroom by $1\frac{1}{2}$ inches. Though the Trident was designed strictly as a road car, a Clipper weighing 32 cwt with all its rollcage and rally equipment was entered in the 1970 London–Sydney Marathon. It reached Yugoslavia before the suspension collapsed.

Below: the Trident Clipper in its original form; at this time, the car was fitted with the Ford '289' 4.7-litre V8, and made the car a very potent piece of machinery indeed

Right: the slightly updated body as used on the later Clippers and Venturers. The Triumph TR6-engined Tycoon also shared the same body. When the Clipper acquired this body, it also received the Chrysler 5.4-litre power unit. Despite being bigger than the Ford unit, its performance was not in the same road-burning class

The early '70s saw Trident wrestling with two problems. A big Ford of Britain strike early in 1971 starved the firm of V6 engines, and exports to the US, France, Spain and Switzerland accordingly suffered. Even more difficult were the demands of continually developing US safety regulations, which gravely hit all limited-production firms.

Nonetheless Trident set about revising its range in the light of the new demands. The Venturer, whose price was now £2300 in kit form, continued with a luxurious specification, though the body now had the opening rear window which was becoming almost obligatory in fastback GT cars. The new Clipper II acquired a Chrysler 5.4-litre V8, to provide the extra power otherwise sapped by the equipment needed for US exhaust emission regulations. Clipper II was also given low-set twin circular headlamps to distinguish it instantly from the smaller-engined car. The specification was just as luxurious as ever, and the £4250 price for a factory-built Clipper included automatic transmission, electric windows and leather upholstery.

In 1971 a new model was introduced—the Trident Tycoon, factory-built at £3250 and fitted with a 2.5-litre Triumph engine to fill the gap left by the short-supply Ford V6. Rectangular headlamps were the only significant external change. But the problems of being a small car manufacturer at a time when the safety and pollution lobbies were hunting the scalps even of the large car makers had by now proved too great, and early in 1972 the firm went into liquidation.

The Trident car was not yet finished, however, and an associate company of Bill Last's, Viking Performance Ltd, took over production, though on a comparatively restricted basis. The firm had previously been responsible only for producing the glassfibre bodies.

In all some 200 Trident cars have been produced, about half of which have been exported. Production has latterly been sporadic and uncertain, and various attempts have been made to put Trident on a sounder footing. At time of writing the car is ostensibly still available and there are plans to revive it more positively in the course of 1975.

EF

Frances racing Mayor

SON OF A FARMER, Maurice Trintignant was born on 30 October 1917, youngest of four brothers, Raoul, René, Louis and Henri. René and Louis raced Bugattis and other machinery and, as an 11-year-old schoolboy, Maurice sometimes acted as a riding mechanic.

In 1938, after his brother Louis was killed, Maurice purchased the very Bugatti T51 in which his brother had been killed and entered his first race, the round-the-houses Pau Grand Prix. Racing against tough opposition he was fifth. He won his second race, the *Grand Prix des Frontières* at Chimay, and repeated this victory in 1939. But for the outbreak of war he would have joined the famous Ecurie Bleue to race Delahayes and Maseratis.

Returning home from the war in the summer of 1945, he rebuilt his beloved Bugatti (which had been dismantled and stored in a barn) and entered the first post-war motor race, the *Coupe de la Liberation* in the Bois de Bologne. He retired when the engine cut out and upon opening the bonnet discovered the fuel filter was clogged—with rat droppings. Evidently, a nest of rats had enjoyed the hospitality of the Bugatti's fuel tank while the car had been dismantled. Race winner Jean-Pierre Wimille enquired of his friend Trintignant the reason for retirement and Maurice said the filter was clogged with *petoule*, a word in the local dialect which meant rat-droppings. Wimille collapsed with laughter and Trintignant was immediately landed with the nickname *Le Petoulet*.

In 1946 the faithful Bugatti—known as *Le*

Below: Maurice Trintignant in action in the 1955 Formula One Ferrari

Grandmère—brought Trintignant second place in the French Championship, and later he turned to various other machinery: Amilcar, Delage, Simca-Gordini. In 1948 he became a member of the Simca-Gordini works team, a team for whom he raced until the end of 1953. However, his first season with Amédée Gordini's cars was almost his last. At Berne, the difficult Swiss road circuit, he was running second in the Formula Two race when his 1500 cc Simca-Gordini spun and crashed. Maurice was hurled from the cockpit and was narrowly missed by four other drivers. He was taken to hospital and was unconscious for eight days. A newspaper carried a story about his 'death' the next day. But he underwent an operation and fifteen days later Maurice Trintignant's name was removed from the critical list. He returned to racing again in 1949.

In 1954 French privateer Louis Rosier bought two Ferraris for Formula One racing and entrusted Trintignant with one; he won the Buenos Aires Grand Prix against Ferrari and Maserati works opposition. By the time the European season got underway he was a member of the official Ferrari team. He won the Hyères 12-hours and the Le Mans 24-hours, the Caen and Rouen Grands Prix and the Tourist Trophy (on scratch with Mike Hawthorn), was second in the Belgian Supercortemaggiori, Pau and Syracuse Grands Prix and at Dakar. Not surprisingly he was Champion of France, a title which he regained in 1955. This was the year his cool, calculated driving won him the Monaco Grand Prix in a Ferrari 625, his first World Championship Grand Prix victory.

For 1956 Trintignant signed with Bugatti, the French firm intending to make a post-war comeback to Grand Prix racing. The Bugatti T251 was a disaster, only running in the French Grand Prix where Trintignant retired with a seized throttle linkage.

It was back to Ferrari for 1957, but his only success was a win in the Reims Formula Two race. At the end of the year he was invited to drive

a BRM P25 in the Moroccan Grand Prix and finished third, silencing critics who thought that at 39, Trintignant was on the decline. Far from it. In 1958 he agreed to race for private entrant Rob Walker in both Formula One and Formula Two. He won the F2 Pau Grand Prix and then the Monaco Grand Prix, beating the Ferrari team. He later won the F1 Caen Grand Prix, the Clermont-Ferrand Formula Two race, was third in the German Grand Prix and was crowned Champion of France once more.

In 1959 Trintignant remained with Walker, finishing second in the United States and third in the Monaco Grand Prix, and piloted a works Aston Martin DBR/300 to second place in the Le Mans 24-hours. For 1960 he agreed to race Aston Martin's new DBR5/250 Formula One car, but it was a disaster. Nevertheless, he won the Buenos Aires Grand Prix in Rob Walker's Cooper T45-Climax and, driving for Porsche, was fourth in the Nürburgring 1000-km. His own Formula Two Cooper T45-Climax was able to provide many excellent results.

In 1961 an underpowered Cooper T45-Maserati entered by Scuderia Serenissima provided little success for Trintignant in the new 1½-litre Formula One. Next season he was back with Rob Walker, but apart from a victory in the Pau Grand Prix with an old Lotus 18/21-Climax, he had no luck. His last success in Formula One was in 1964 when, at 46, he was a rousing fifth in the German Grand Prix in his own privately-entered BRM P57. His last competitive racing appearance was in the 1965 Le Mans 24-hours where he retired his Ford GT40 after difficulties with his gearbox.

But Maurice Trintignant was more than a racing driver. He took control of his family's vineyard (naming the wine *Le Petoulet*) and developed it into a thriving concern. In 1959 he was also elected mayor of Vergèze, and a year later he was created a Chevalier of the Legion of Honour for his services to France.   MK

Aristocratic race-ace

WOLFGANG GRAF BERGHE VON TRIPS was an aristocrat, a tall blond German Count who was a lover of fast cars and of life itself. Familiarly known as 'Taffy', von Trips survived a succession of high-speed accidents until he crashed to his death at Monza in 1961.

After having dabbled in racing for a number of years, Von Trips entered an old Porsche in some rallies. His success persuaded him to contact Porsche's racing director, Huschke von Hanstein, to ask for free parts to modify his machine. Von Hanstein offered Von Trips a drive in the 1954 Mille Miglia as co-driver to Hampel. Against all odds, the pair were second in the 1500 cc GT class and the first 1300 cc car to finish. He later acquired a 1500 cc engine for his Porsche Super and entered his first race at Nürburgring with the bill for the engine still unpaid. He won then settled the account. Soon he had won the German GT Championship.

In 1955 both Porsche and Mercedes-Benz smiled on Von Trips. He was reserve driver for Porsche at Le Mans and after some impressive performances in his 1300 cc Porsche he was offered a works Mercedes-Benz 300SL for the GT race at the Swedish Grand Prix meeting. He led for 16 of the 20 laps before the brakes failed, thereby earning a place in the sports-racing car team of 300SLRs in the Tourist Trophy at Dundrod. Co-driving with Kling and André, Simon he was third.

With Mercedes' withdrawal from motor racing at the end of 1955 it was back to Porsche for 1956. In a works Porsche 550RS he won the 1500 cc class in the Sebring 12-hours, Nürburgring 1000-km and Le Mans 24-hours. This led to an invitation to race for Ferrari. He was second with Peter Collins in the Swedish Grand Prix sports-car race and was invited to pilot a Formula One Lancia-Ferrari D50 in the Italian Grand at Monza. In practice the steering broke at high speed, Von Trips being thrown clear of the rolling wreckage and emerging almost unhurt.

In 1957 Von Trips remained with Ferrari in both Formula One and sports cars. He was sixth in the Argentine Grand Prix, second in the Mille Miglia only 3 m 1 s behind Piero Taruffi and bitter in the Monaco Grand Prix when his engine blew-up with only 11 laps to go. After being absent due to a spinal injury, at the Nürburgring 1000-km, he was back in late August and went on to finish third in the Italian Grand Prix and third in the sports-car Venezuelan Grand Prix. Driving for Porsche, he participated in three end-of-season European Hill-climb Championship events, winning the Swiss Mountain Grand Prix and at Mont Parnes and taking a second at Aosta-Gran San Barnardo.

The format was similar in 1958. Best placing in Grand Prix racing was third in the French Grand Prix, while in sports cars he was second in the Buenos Aires 1000-km and third in the Targa Florio and Nürburgring 1000-km. He won the European Hill-climb Championship, his works Porsche winning at Mount Parnassus, Monte Bendone and Gaisberg. In the Rheims 12-hours for GT cars he shared a Ferrari Berlinetta with fellow-German Wolfgang Seidel into third place. However, in September another accident temporarily put him out of racing: his Ferrari Dino 246 collided with Harry Schell's BRM P25 on the opening lap, crashed and Von Trips broke a leg.

Enzo Ferrari dropped Von Trips from his team the next year, leaving the German free to race for Porsche in sports-car and Formula Two racing. Best result was a second in the Tourist Trophy at Goodwood, although it was galling when he broke down on the last lap of the Targa Florio when leading. 'Taffy' von Trips blotted his copybook at Monaco, where he gave the new Formula Two Porsche its *début* and spun on the second lap, causing a pile-up involving the other two Formula Two cars in the race! In December he was back with Ferrari for the United States Grand Prix. After colliding with team-mate Tony Brooks on the first lap he recovered to finish seventh. Continuing to drive for Ferrari in 1960, Von Trips found the front-engined Formula One machines inferior to the latest Coopers and Lotuses and had to be satisfied with minor placings, best being a fourth in Portugal. In Formula Two, he won the Solitude Grand Prix and, making a 'guest appearance' for Porsche was second in the F2 German Grand Prix at Nürburgring. He was also second for Ferrari in the Buenos Aires 1000-km and Targa Florio sports-car races, but ran out of fuel at Le Mans.

For 1961 Ferrari were ahead of their British rivals, providing Phil Hill, Wolfgang von Trips and Richie Ginther with cars capable of winning the World Championship. Von Trips won the Dutch Grand Prix at Zandvoort, becoming the first German to win a *grande épreuve* since 1939, and later won the British Grand Prix after a brilliant performance on the sodden Aintree track. Into the Italian Grand Prix at Monza, Von Trips had a one-point lead in the championship. Entering the Parabolica on lap 2 Jim Clark moved to overtake Von Trips' Ferrari Dino 156 under braking. The two cars touched at 140 mph and spun. Clark's car halted safely, almost undamaged. Von Trips' hurtled up the banking into the spectator area, killing fourteen people before plunging back on to the track, overturning and killing its occupant.

MK

Below: Wolfgang von Trips driving the 1958 F1 Ferrari at Silverstone

A TRADITIONAL SPORTING STYLE

The Triumph company is perhaps best known for producing motor cars with a traditionally sporting flavour

THOUGH THE FIRST TRIUMPH motor car did not go into production until 1923, the firm's foundations reach back to a German immigrant's arrival in England in 1884. After a year in London, Siegfried Bettmann, established his own company to import various German goods. Only one of his several agencies, which dealt with sewing machines, flourished, and Bettmann hopefully turned to bicycles, which were the latest thing.

He contracted with a Birmingham cycle maker, William Andrews, for the manufacture of cycles which his company would distribute. But what to call it? Bettmann wanted a name that made sense in all European countries, and decided on 'Triumph'. He was not long satisfied with merely distributing the Triumph cycle, however, and soon established a works in Coventry to make it. Again Bettmann was dissatisfied—the internal-combustion engine was coming along, and he wanted to be part of the new industry. He persuaded Dunlop to inject some capital into Bettmann and Co, and in 1901 the first Triumph motor cycle was produced. A whole series of successful models followed. Bettmann, now a naturalised Briton, became mayor of Coventry and President of the British Cycle and Motor-cycle Manufacturers' Union.

After World War I Bettmann decided to expand into car manufacture and bought out the local Dawson Car Co. The first car to carry the Triumph Globe badge was 10–20 hp Weymann-bodied saloon with a Ricardo-designed four-cylinder engine. Its bore and stroke of 63.5 × 110 mm provided 1393 cc capacity and developed 23.4 bhp at 3000 rpm driving though a cone clutch and a four-speed gearbox. A two-seater sports version was introduced the same year. Clock, speedometer, choice of leather or cloth trim, and mohair-twill top established Triumph as a firm offering 'something extra'.

A bigger car, the 13–30 hp with 1873 cc engine, was produced in 1924, and had the distinction of being the first British car with Lockheed hydraulic brakes as standard equipment. These external contracting-band brakes operated on all four wheels—another unusual feature. Two years later a yet bigger Triumph joined the range—the four-cylinder 2169 cc Fifteen, with a very square and upright saloon body.

While these first three Triumph models were sound enough, and the design team had proved its willingness to innovate, Bettmann really sought to build 'the big car in perfect miniature', and it was the Super Seven of 1927 that really made the firm's name. It had an 832 cc side-valve engine with three-bearing crankshaft, three-speed gearbox, semi-elliptic front and quarter-elliptic rear springs, and Lockheed four-wheel brakes. Cruising speed was 50 mph. Wheelbase was only 81 inches and with a cost of £150 it replaced the 10/20 model.

The Super Seven, produced at a rate of 75 a week by about 800 workers, so dominated Triumph's programme that the Fifteen was displaced. The Seven took over the firm's Priory Street, Coventry, works and the Fifteen production went to Stoke, which had previously produced bodies only.

Below: a view of the Triumph 15 of 1928. It was powered by a four-cylinder, side-valve engine of 2170 cc. The 15 models were produced from 1927 until 1930

Below: the first four-wheel Triumph motor car ever produced was the 10/20 which appeared in 1923; it was fitted with a 1393 cc, side-valve, four-cylinder motor

Below: the Super Seven model of 1928 was the car which really made the Triumph company's name; it was powered by a four-cylinder, side-valve engine of 747 cc

Bottom left: the prototype Triumph Silver Bullet TRX of 1950

Bottom right: a 1935 Triumph Gloria saloon. These were available with four or six cylinders

With the introduction of the Super Seven, Triumph became involved in competition motoring. Although the little 832 cc car caused a quiet smile or two when it first sidled up to bigger rivals, the three-bearing crankshaft, Lockheed brakes and tough construction soon made the doubters change their tune, and the Super Seven made its mark in trials, hill-climbs and even at Brooklands races.

In the 1928 Land's End Trial, Donald Healey won a silver medal in a Super Seven—the start of a long and successful association between Healey and Triumph. In the same year Gordon England (who was also responsible for one of the many variants offered by outside firms on the Super Seven's ladder chassis) entered the Seven in a 40-lap JCC High Speed Trial, which included the notorious Test Hill, and won a Gold Medal. The following year saw more successes—Victor Horsman won the 46th Long Handicap on the Brooklands outer circuit at the BARC Easter meeting, with an average speed of 78.25 mph. His Super Seven had a special single-seater body with a cowled radiator and tapered tail and head fairing. He won again at the circuit's closing meeting for 1930.

Healey's next outstanding outing in a Triumph was in the 1929 Monte Carlo Rally. He made Monte five minutes after the control had closed, having driven from Berlin. The following year, immediately after finishing fourth in the Riga Rally, Healey set off for Monte from Tallinn, got three hours sleep in the course of the 2160-mile run, and finished seventh overall with the best British performance.

The Triumph penchant for out-of-the-ordinary cars was now well established. A supercharged Seven was introduced as a standard model in 1929, with a Cozette blower mounted on the left of the engine, which was claimed to develop 32 bhp at 4500 rpm and give a 65 mph maximum speed—all for £250. By 1930 a quarter of all Triumph production was being exported and Super Sevens were figuring largely in Australian city-to-city record runs and in Australian and South African trials.

A Gnat sports two-seater version was introduced in 1930, and Triumph chased the success of the rival Wolseley six-cylinder Hornet with a small six of their own, the 1202 cc Scorpion, which installed its 56.5 × 80mm side-valve unit in a lengthened Super Seven chassis.

The Super Nine was introduced in 1932 with a Coventry Climax four-cylinder 1018 cc 32 bhp engine with overhead inlet and side exhaust valves. This engine also went into a new Triumph sports model, the Southern Cross, named in recognition of the firm's Australian sales and competition successes. There was a notable European success for this engine—the first of a number of Coventry Climax units in Triumph cars—when Mrs Margaret Vaughan took the Ladies' Cup in the 1932 Monte Carlo event driving a Nine with a Royston drophead coupé body. She won her prize in spite of stopping to help a crashed crew and setting four broken legs.

Donald Healey joined the company as chief experimental engineer, in 1933, with a strong sporting approach to his job. After a new range of Triumphs was introduced in 1934—the Gloria, supposedly named after a famous London mannequin of the day, and offered in 1087 cc four-cylinder and 1476 cc six-cylinder form—Healey put seven of them into the Monte Carlo Rally of that year. All finished, and Healey himself took third overall place and won the 1500 Class prize. In the Alpine Rally of the following year the three works Gloria cars took the manufacturers' team prize in the 1100 cc class and two drivers—Healey and Maurice Newnham (who was later to become managing director)—received awards for having incurred no

penalty points at all.

A Gloria Speed Model soon followed, with a triple-carburettor engine and open four-seater bodywork, and 1934 saw the introduction of yet another sporting Triumph, a two-litre supercharged straight-eight Dolomite with body style and engine design 'borrowed' from Alfa Romeo. The production programme stumbled at this point, however—with so many sporting ideas sparking at the same time it is not hard to see why—and the Dolomite was dropped after only three prototypes had been built; though the irrepressible Healey took one on the Monte Carlo Rally of 1935—and was lucky to escape uninjured when the car was demolished by a train on a level crossing. His competitions manager, J. C. Ridley, managed to avoid trains and finished second overall in another car, taking the 1500 cc class award. In the following year Healey took another Dolomite to eighth place in the Monte. Miss Joan Richmond, in another Triumph, was second in the 1500 cc class.

All these successes in southern Europe led to the renaming of the Gloria Speed Model as the Monte Carlo Tourer—while in 1935 the special-equipment version of the same car was called the Vitesse. Inevitably, Healey took a Vitesse rallying, and won a Glacier Award in the 1936 Alpine event for incurring no penalty points in an outstanding performance, in his 14/60 saloon against sports cars. Another Triumph driver in this event, finishing fifteenth in a Southern Cross two-seater, was Tony Rolt.

Further competition entries were curtailed by financial problems, though regular class wins were registered in British, Scottish and Welsh rallies for several years. Triumph concentrated on production cars with the development of the Gloria range until 1937, when the Dolomite name was revived for a new range powered by Triumph's own overhead-valve engines—a four-cylinder 75 × 100 mm unit with a 1767 cc capacity in the Dolomite 14/60 and Roadster coupé, and a six-cylinder 1991 cc engine with

65 × 100mm pots in the Dolomite Two-litre. Bodies were of steel sheet over wooden frames, there being insufficient capital to go over to steel pressings, and though the Dolomites sold well and had a good reputation in the market, the motor industry went into the immediate pre-war doldrums, and Triumph failed. There were brief efforts to merge with Riley, also in deep trouble, and Riley and Triumph both found themselves in the hands of the receiver.

Both were saved—Riley was bought by Lord Nuffield as an addition to his Morris, MG and Wolseley

string, and Triumph was purchased by the Sheffield steel firm, Thomas W. Ward. War broke out soon afterwards, and any plans Ward had for getting into car production were scotched. The old Coventry works were all but flattened in one of the heavy blitzes to which that city was subjected, and most of the old Triumph records were totally destroyed. Nonetheless the firm was active in aircraft production and built more than a thousand Mosquito aircraft.

It was the plywood construction of this light fast Pathfinder aircraft that shaped Triumph's immediate

Top: a 1939 Triumph Dolomite roadster

Above left: front view of the popular Triumph Gloria sports saloon

Above right: the Triumph 1800 Roadster of 1945

Top: a Triumph Southern Cross sports two-seater of 1935

Above: the Triumph Mayflower saloon, introduced in 1950, was powered by a four-cylinder, side-valve, 1247 cc engine

post-war car production, for after Sir John Black of the Standard Motor Co bought Triumph from Ward in 1944, it was one of the first British car makers to resume production with new models. There was the 1800 Renown, whose razor-edge body styling was a direct legacy of the wartime handling of plywood panels, and at the same time the firm also returned to conspicuously rounded contours with the 1800 Roadster, whose bulbous aluminium front wings and long bonnet attracted eager crowds wherever it appeared during those post-war years.

Though the Renown served Triumph conspicuously well until 1955 in the medium-large saloon category, and was particularly liked by professional men, it was the Roadster that most reflected the post-war public need for some racy expression of the old pleasures and the new freedoms.

The Roadster was not particularly speedy—its 1.8 ohv long-stroke engine produced only 65 bhp and 75 mph—but it had highly individual looks, boasted an American-style three-at-a-pinch bench seat, two extra dickey-type seats behind the hood with their own pop-up screen, a very solid tubular chassis, transverse springs in front and semi-elliptics at the rear, good road stability, fair all-round visibility, an easily-handled hood, wind-up windows and a full complement of switches. Only its column-mounted gearchange (which admittedly made life easier for the centre of three front occupants) was difficult for the British driver to take.

This Roadster, and latterly the Renown, acquired the ubiquitous Standard Vanguard 2.2-litre engine in 1949, a much squarer overhead-valve unit which produced another five bhp and gave the Roadster an extra 10 mph or so—not a lot in today's terms, but a real boost at the time, when every motorist's first question was 'What'll she do?' And no one even dreamed of blanket speed limits. Some 2000 Roadsters were built in all.

While the Renown sustained Triumph's reputation for solid-quality motoring, the firm also sought to produce quality in miniature, in the way originally outlined by the founder Siegfried Bettmann, who had handed over the managing directorship in 1933, dabbled in Triumph cycles through the late '30s and retired properly in 1939. Bettmann died, an honoured Coventrarian, in 1951, at the age of 87.

The car that tried to reproduce this small-style luxury was the Mayflower, with an aluminium body by Mulliner, and repeating the razor-edge approach (at least one example was produced using Mosquito-style plywood, in fact).

Aluminium was favoured, incidentally, not for lightness but because of the post-war steel shortage.

The Mayflower had a conventional 1247 cc engine of 63 × 100 mm cylinders, gave a modest 38 bhp and was just as modestly priced at £395. Its heavy-looking body, which contained a surprising amount of space despite a mere 84-inch wheelbase, gained a lot of admirers and also a lot of detractors, but Triumph managed to make and sell some 32,000, including 500 convertible models. It did not sell to enthusiasts—it took 26 seconds to labour up to 60 mph from rest—a marked contrast to the things Triumph had in mind.

At the 1950 London Motor Show a new Roadster was revealed. Its aerodynamic light-alloy body with concealed headlamps earned it the nickname of Silver Bullet, though officially it was the TRX. It abounded in electrical and hydraulic gadgetry—the seat adjustment was hydraulic, the windows and soft top were electric, the headlamps were behind electrically-operated panels, and the bonnet was opened and closed by means of an electrically powered hydraulic ram.

The problems presented by this exciting but complicated arrangement started with an embarrassing incident in front of Princess Margaret at the Motor Show. No one had told the demonstrator, the new Triumph Chairman, Sir John Black that the various functions of the control switches had been switched around on the prototype. An electric fire broke out under the bonnet of the car, one of only three built,

Above: the Triumph Mayflower saloon of 1950 pictured at the Earls Court Motor Show The car cost £375 plus £104 purchase tax

shorting all the wiring, and depriving the driver of any means of raising the bonnet. Sir John was forced to stand by and watch the car burn out more or less thoroughly. The penalties of over sophistication were obvious to all. Material shortages because of the Korean war sealed the car's fate.

At this time Triumph decided to go for the US sports-

Above: during the 1950s, the Italian designer, Michelotti, produced this prototype which was based on Triumph mechanicals

car market and decided on an entirely new model. It was put together in time for the 1952 London Motor Show, and was called the TR1. The car was basically 'pinched' from Triumph's associated company, Standard, resting on a Standard 8 chassis frame with a Standard Vanguard engine and a bob-tailed body. It was an immediate disaster—it failed to produce any power and handled badly, and BRM's Ken Richardson was hastily called in to sort it out. This he did within three months, replacing the Standard 8 frame with a stiffer chassis, widening the body by two inches, drawing the rounded tail out into a shape that allowed some boot-space, and experimenting with the engine, steering, brake and damper settings. The result was the famous TR2, which quickly made a 115 mph run at Jabbeke in road trim and 125 mph in high-speed trim. Its engine would take any degree of hammering, and it sold for £555—outstanding value even in those days.

While the TR2 was gaining in popularity among young sports-car enthusiasts—this was the period when every young blood needed a drophead sports car to complete his wardrobe—the firm was getting back into the good old pre-war competition stride. In 1954 the RAC Rally went outright to Johnny Wallwork in a TR2—its first competitive appearance. Mary Walker won the Ladies' Prize in another TR2. Richardson himself took another TR2 on the Mille Miglia and finished 28th out of 365 starters by 'just motoring beautifully the whole way, using only a quart of oil'.

The TRs, moving into TR3 and 3A versions through the '50s, continued to win. In one Alpine Rally, six TRs entered and all finished, taking the team prize and five Alpine Cups, the sixth failing to gain a cup when a wheel came loose. TR ruggedness and reliability became a by-word. The engine went into several pretty

low-volume sports GT cars of the period—Swallow Doretti, Peerless, Warwick. In Italy Michelotti designed a GT fixed-head coupe which Vignale produced in small numbers, the Italia, on the TR3 chassis and running gear.

In 1959 the TR was used as the basis for a Le Mans car, the TRS, with 'five-decker-sandwich' engine

—sump, crankcase extension, crankcase cylinder block and head each stacked on top of the other—of 1985 cc 90 × 78 mm with 9.25 to 1 compression, and producing 150 bhp. Bulging cam covers on top earned the engine the nickname Sabrina (after a well endowed showgirl of the day) among Triumph personnel.

Three of these cars, with stock TR3 body to catch the imaginations—and wallets—of the buying public (Triumph research showed them to be mainly in their late-forties and seeking to re-capture their lost youth) competed at Le Mans, but all retired through mechanical failure. The following year they were back with new glassfibre Michelotti bodies. This time they took second, fourth and fifth class positions, one of the cars being timed at 129 mph down the Mulsanne Straight, and averaging 103.8 mph. Finally, in 1961, all the kinks were ironed out and the TRS took the team prize, the first one home making ninth overall, and ahead of all other British entries.

Triumph toyed for a while with the notion of introducing a production TRS as a top-of-range addition to the TR4, which replaced the TR3 in 1961. Some tooling was ordered, but in the uncertainty of the period just before Leyland took the firm over in December 1960, the car, code-named Zoom, was dropped.

Meanwhile Triumph had not been idle on the saloon front. Anything but—1959 saw the introduction of the Herald. Designed by Michelotti, it had a traditional chassis and seven-section body designed for quick and cheap replacement in the event of damage. Insurance companies loved it. Suspension was independent all round—wishbones at the front, swing-axles at the rear—the turning circle of 24 feet rivalled that of the London taxi, and engine access was total, the whole bonnet and front wing section swinging upwards and

forwards (a ploy which Peerless and Warwick had used). The 948 cc unit produced 38.5 bhp in the saloon version, and 50.5 bhp in the coupé and convertible versions. The Herald went into 1200 and stripped-down S versions in 1961, 12/50 version with 1147 cc engine and the first standard sunshine roof in its class in 1963, and then to 13/60 with a 1296 cc unit in 1967. By

Below: the Triumph 1300TC of 1967; this body style was first introduced on the 1300 model of 1965 and was later used on the 1500 and Toledo models. The 1300TC was powered by a four-cylinder, twin-carburettor engine of 1296 cc, which developed 75 bhp at 6000 rpm

Above left: a 1968 Triumph GT6 MkII. The car was fitted with a six-cylinder engine of 1998 cc which developed 104 bhp at 5300 rpm

Above: the TR4 that was in production between 1961 and 1965; it was updated to TR4A specification when it acquired independent rear suspension and four extra bhp to add to the 100 it already had

Above right: the Dolomite Sprint was introduced in 1973 and acquired much acclaim for its performance and its technically advanced engine; the car's two-litre unit had a four-valve-per-cylinder system operated by one overhead camshaft

Right: the Spitfire as it appeared in Mk I and Mk II guises; it used a tuned 1147 cc Herald engine

the time the Herald was replaced by the Toledo in 1970, something like half a million Heralds in all versions had been built.

Impressed as the world had been with the 948 cc Herald in 1959, it was not generally known that at the time Triumph had been aiming for a very simple small car designed to give 60 mph and 60 mpg—the '60/60' car has become one of the catch-phrase ambitions of the post-energy crisis—to compete directly with the VW Beetle which was then making its presence felt in many markets.

There was another prototype too—the Zebu, a six-cylinder car of two litres with transaxle, Macpherson strut front and trailing-link rear suspension. The transaxle was abandoned in favour of a normal front gearbox because of torsional problems, and two body styles were toyed with, one of them very close to the cut back rear window which Ford adopted on the Anglia. The Zebu foundered when Triumph hit its pre-Leyland-takeover cash shortages in 1960.

But the mechanical experience was not wasted, for it proved useful in developing a new six-cylinder car that did make it—the 1.6-litre four-headlamp Vitesse version of the Herald, launched in 1962. Other Zebu lessons, especially about suspension, were applied to a new larger saloon, the 2000 of 1963. The 2000 used the Standard Vanguard six-cylinder engine in a completely new unitary body, with independent suspension all round and a good standard of equipment and comfort.

Meanwhile the TR sports-car series was backed up by a second string. As the TR moved into squarer Michelotti-designed 4 series in 1961, a two-seater based

on the Herald took shape—the Spitfire. This car utilised a lot of Herald components, and inherited the saloon's tiny turning circle and generous luggage space.

Development was reciprocal—the special camshaft of the Spitfire was used when the Herald moved into 12/50 form in 1963. The Spitfire was progressively refined in the engine compartment and in styling, with a Mk II appearing in 1964, Mk III in 1967 and a Mk IV in 1970.

As the Vitesse developed out of the Herald, it was inevitable that Triumph engineers should seek to do the same six-cylinder exercise with the Spitfire. The result was the GT6 of 1966—the same year that the Vitesse was uprated to two-litres. GT6 improvements latterly paralleled those of the Spitfire. Both Spitfire and GT6 proved enduringly appealing on both home and foreign markets, and in March 1975 the Spitfire had its best month ever in the US market, where success has been decisive to continuing British sports-car manufacture. American buyers also took large quantities of the later developments in the TR series—the TR5 of 1967, which employed the fuel-injection six-cylinder 2500 engine that also found its way into the 2000 saloon to create the top Triumph, the 2.5 PI of 1968, and the TR6 of 1969. A TR7, with dramatic wedge styling by Harris Mann, was introduced in 1974, to be sold initially in the US market, with TR6 production continuing in parallel for some time.

One of the immediate results of Leyland's takeover in 1960 had been the reorganisation of the competitions department, this time under Graham Robson, and with a slim budget. TR4s were the department's first weapon, but had a patchy career, being neither fast nor rugged enough; in 1963 Robson added Vitesses to the armoury, and the following year rally Spitfires, Le Mans Spitfires and 2000 saloons.

The Spitfires did particularly well. The Le Mans cars used aluminium bodyshells and glassfibre hard-tops modelled on the GT6 which was by then in proto-type form. Special nose shapes were designed to cleave the Le Mans airstreams, and power was increased to 98 bhp—though little had to be done to the suspension. These cars amazed everyone by topping 130 mph down the straight and lapping Le Mans at 100 mph. In the race, two crashed and one finished, averaging 95 mph.

service back-up costing the earth and being all but necessary if a team wanted to earn top placings. Leyland was not prepared to put the money in, and the Triumph challenge thereafter became sporadic. The firm's World Cup Rally challenge was with 2.5s based largely on the work done in the mid '60s.

Latterly the Dolomite Sprint has been upholding Triumph's sporting name, a car prepared by Ralph Broad and driven by Andy Rouse gaining the 1974 British Saloon Car Championship in the two-litre class.

The Dolomite Sprint was one of a line of cars stemming from the front-wheel drive 1300 model of 1965, a medium saloon which yet again re-echoed the old Bettmann tenet of producing large-car quality in scaled-down form.

In 1970 a revised but similarly styled bodyshell was

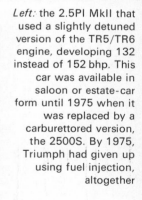

Below: the first British production car to be fitted with fuel injection as standard equipment was the TR5. Its 2.5-litre, six-cylinder engine, sporting Lucas injection, replaced the Standard Vanguard-based unit of its predecessor

Left: the 2.5PI MkII that used a slightly detuned version of the TR5/TR6 engine, developing 132 instead of 152 bhp. This car was available in saloon or estate-car form until 1975 when it was replaced by a carburettored version, the 2500S. By 1975, Triumph had given up using fuel injection, altogether

By the time Robson left in 1965 the rally version of the 2000 introduced in 1963 was shaping well, and with Finn Simo Lampinen signed up among the up-and-coming drivers they were ready for some outright wins.

But rallying was getting into its big-time swing, with drivers paid on a new and handsome scale and full

introduced with a new engine range. The 1300 became the Toledo, with rear-wheel drive—it replaced the last of the Heralds—and there was a front-wheel drive 1500 and a 1750 slant-four rear-wheel drive Dolomite whose engine had been sold to Saab since 1967 for use in their 99 model. The difference in layout within this range

was finally resolved when the 1500 was given rear-wheel drive. The engine was also uprated with twin carburettors.

The Dolomite engine as used in the four-door car was of 1854 cc and in 1973 the Sprint was introduced with a 16-valve four-cylinder 1998 cc engine with single camshaft lying between the valve rows. The Sprint, while proving its mettle on the circuits, was also widely regarded as one of the most exciting but civilised road cars produced in Britain in the mid '70s.

One model remains to be described. Triumph always leaned towards the sporting side of motoring, and while the robust but comparatively unexciting 2000 was sustaining Triumph's name in the executive market, plans were afoot for a coupé version. A 2000 was sent to Giovanni Michelotti, whose affiliation with Triumph went back to the original Herald and to the switch from the rounded contours of the early TRs to the squarer TR4.

Michelotti's brief was to produce a car to stimulate interest at the Geneva Motor Show, but what he styled on a shortened 2000 saloon floorpan so excited Triumph executives that they bypassed the show plans and had the car whisked straight to Coventry for their production experts to look at. At that stage it was powered by the 2000's straight-six engine. But Triumph were already toying with the 'other half' of the Dolomite slant-four engine—in other words, a V8 was being knitted together—and it was obvious that this unit should go in the proposed coupé. In enlarged 3-litre form it did, and with uprated 2000 components to cope with the extra power, the new car was launched in 1970 as the Stag.

The Stag, aimed substantially at the US market but never to take off in the sort of quantity which those initially enthusiastic executives dreamed of, did introduce a new approach to the roll-over bar. The first design, incorporated as part of the general concern for safety standards which public debate in America was causing, was of the conventional race-type—a fairly simple hoop situated amidships. Such were the doubts at Triumph over it that it was a bolt-on affair which the owner might remove if he wished.

But torsional problems developed in the body, and since it was felt that the motoring public at the proposed Stag level had outgrown the scuttle-shake which for years had been a feature of open cars, the hoop roll-over bar was endowed with a leg that fixed to the centre of the top of the windscreen. The roll-over bar thus became a roll-over cage—the first of its type to be marketed by a car maker. And it proved in effect that the roof could be sliced off a saloon (the bottom end of the Stag being in effect a 2000) and replaced by a three-legged cage.

This had a profound bearing on thinking at the time, since it was thought highly likely that the United States—the biggest world market for drophead cars—would ban convertible cars unless they were provided with roll-over protection which could be proved to offer at least as much of a safe passenger compartment as a saloon.

Problems with hood noise even at moderate speeds provoked Triumph to design a fastback fixed-head version fairly soon after the soft-top came out, but the economic climate was forcing the firm—now embroiled in the general low-investment situation which was to bring British Leyland on its knees to the government's door—to be very choosey over model policy.

Management acrobatics at British Leyland made Triumph part of the Specialist Car Division and then of Rover–Triumph. The latter structure was having a great deal of finance pumped into it before the re-formation of British Leyland under the terms of the Ryder Report called for the Government to assess whether and on what terms the Corporation should have public money injected into it.

At the time of writing the report's proposal that the whole of British Leyland's car operation should be drawn together into one car division was being implemented, Triumph being a part of it.

The Triumph 2000/2500 series was expected to be replaced in 1976 by a model which would also replace the Rover 2000/3500 models with which the Triumphs had for some years been competing. EF

STAG

By 1970, Triumph had secured a reputation for building 'gap fillers', directed at unoccupied niches in the British car market. The company had early seen the wisdom of production—and profitability—in areas with little competition.

It was 1970 that saw the introduction of the Stag, a smooth and luxurious tourer with a soft top that had few competitors world wide and none at all in Britain.

The power unit for the Stag is a 3-litre two-cam V8, which is based on two four-cylinder Dolomite/Saab 99 cylinder blocks with, naturally, two Dolomite-type heads. The power output for the engine is 145 bhp at 5700 rpm and 167 lb ft at 3500 rpm, delivering a top speed of 121 mph. Overdrive on the upper two ratios is standard on the manual version in Great Britain. Acceleration from 0–50 mph is accomplished in 6.9 s and the car is capable of over 20 mpg of petrol.

The Stag uses an independent front suspension layout by MacPherson struts, lower leading-arm wishbones and an anti-roll bar, while the rear is independent by semi-trailing arms, coil springs and telescopic dampers.

Steering is by power-assisted rack and pinion, with three turns from lock to lock, and braking is by servo-assisted front discs and rear drums.

Apart from the option of the two transmissions, a four-speed manual or a Borg-Warner 35 automatic unit, the car is available with or without a removable hardtop fitting over the standard convertible version.

ENGINE Front-mounted, water-cooled 90° V8. 86 mm (3.39 in) bore × 64.5 mm (2.54 in) stroke = 2997 cc (182.9 cu in). Maximum power (DIN) 145 bhp at 5700 rpm; maximum torque (DIN) 167 lb ft at 3500 rpm. Cast-iron cylinder block and light-alloy heads. Compression ratio 9.25:1. 5 main bearings. 2 valves per cylinder operated direct by a single camshaft per cylinder head. 2 Stromberg 175 COS (E) V sidedraught single-barrel carburettors.

TRANSMISSION Single-dry-plate clutch and 4-speed manual gearbox with overdrive (standard on British market, optional on others), or torque converter and Borg-Warner 35 automatic unit. Maximum ratio of converter at stall 2.275. Ratios for manual, 1st 2.995, 2nd 2.100, 3rd 1.386, 4th 1, rev 3.369:1. Ratio for overdrive (working on 3rd and 4th gears) 0.797:1. Ratios for automatic 1st 2.390, 2nd 1.450, 3rd 1, rev 2.090:1.

CHASSIS Integral.

SUSPENSION Front—independent by MacPherson struts, lower leading-arm wishbones and an anti-roll bar, rear—independent by semi-trailing arms, coil springs and telescopic dampers.

STEERING Power-assisted rack and pinion. Turns from lock to lock 3.

BRAKES Servo-assisted front discs and rear drums.

WHEELS 14 in × 5 in steel or light alloy.

TYRES 185HR × 14.

DIMENSIONS AND WEIGHT Wheelbase 100 in; track—front 52.60 in, rear 53 in; length 173.75 in; width 63.50 in; height 49.53 in; ground clearance 4.02 in; dry weight 2640 lb; turning circle between walls 34.1 ft; fuel tank capacity 13.9 gals.

BODY 2-door, 4-seater convertible. Hardtop version available.

PERFORMANCE Maximum speed 121 mph. Acceleration 0–50 mph 6.9 secs. Fuel consumption approximately 21 mpg.

DOLOMITE SPRINT

The body shell of the Triumph Dolomite Sprint was already eight years old when the car appeared in 1973. It was first seen clothing the front-wheel-drive 1300 in 1965. Then, variously, the body was fitted to the 1300 TC, the Toledo, the 1500, 1500 TC and the Dolomite.

When the new Dolomite Sprint was finally introduced, it was powered by an amazing 127 bhp two-litre engine. Based on the cast-iron/alloy unit used in the ordinary Dolomite and the Saab 99, this new engine differed in that the single-overhead camshaft opened four valves per cylinder; two in each cylinder direct and the other two by an ingenious crossover rocker system. This meant that the Sprint could have four-valve breathing on one camshaft, whereas most other engines employing quad valves needed two camshafts.

The 1998 cc engine (exactly the same capacity as the six-cylinder 2000 engine) drives through either a four-speed manual with overdrive or a three-speed Borg-Warner 65 automatic unit to the rear wheels.

The Sprint uses an independent front suspension system, with wishbones, acting as lower trailing links, coil springs, an anti-roll bar and telescopic dampers, while the rear is non-independent by a rigid axle, lower trailing arms, upper oblique torque arms, coil springs, an anti-roll bar and telescopic dampers.

ENGINE Front-mounted, water-cooled straight-four. 90.3 mm (3.56 in) bore × 78 mm (3.07 in) stroke = 1998 cc (122 cu in). Maximum power (DIN) 127 bhp at 5700 rpm; maximum torque (DIN) 122 lb ft at 4500 rpm. Cast-iron cylinder block and light-alloy head. Compression ratio 9.5:1. 5 main bearings.

4 valves per cylinder operated, directly and by crossover push-rods, by a single-overhead camshaft. 2 SU HS 6 sidedraught single-barrel carburettors.

TRANSMISSION Single-dry-plate and 4-speed manual gearbox, with overdrive operating on the upper two ratios, or Borg-Warner 65 3-speed automatic unit. Ratios for manual 1st 2.990, 2nd 2.100, 3rd 1.390, 4th 1, rev 3.370:1. Overdrive ratio 0.792:1. Ratios for automatic, 1st 2.390, 2nd 1.450, 1.450, 3rd 1, rev 2.090:1. Hypoid-bevel final drive. Ratio 3.450:1.

CHASSIS Integral with front subframe.

SUSPENSION Front—independent by wishbones, acting as lower trailing links, coil springs, an anti-roll bar and telescopic dampers, rear—non-independent by a rigid axle, lower trailing arms, upper oblique torque arms, coil springs, an anti-roll bar and telescopic dampers.

STEERING Rack and pinion. Turns from lock to lock 3.75.

BRAKES Servo-assisted front discs and rear drums.

WHEELS 13 in × 5.5 in light-alloy.

TYRES 175/70 HR × 13.

DIMENSIONS AND WEIGHT Wheelbase 96.62 in; track—front 53.94 in, rear—50.79 in; height 54 in; ground clearance 4.25 in; dry weight 2123 lb; turning circle between walls 31.7 ft; fuel tank capacity 12.5 gals.

BODY Saloon. 4-door, 4–5 seater.

PERFORMANCE Maximum speed 117 mph. Acceleration 0–60 mph 8.5 secs. Fuel consumption approximately 26 mpg.

CHEAPER THAN WALKING?

Trojan cars were noted for their thriftiness and proved very popular with drivers searching for economy and reliability

'CAN YOU AFFORD TO WALK?' demanded the advertising of the Trojan, which was possibly the most successful utility car of all time. In fact, the company even put out a hilarious advertising film which purported to show that the operating costs of the Trojan were substantially less than the cost of repairs to the shoes of a keen walker. It was all a little unconvincing and left one with the impression that the man who bought a Trojan did so because he could not afford to buy a car . . .

The Trojan was the brainchild of Leslie Hounsfield, who had begun his engineering career as a Whitworth scholar assisting the steam traction pioneer, Colonel R. E. B. Crompton develop a steam wagon for gun haulage in the Boer War.

The engine developed by the two men followed internal combustion wagon lines and was very different from the normal pattern of traction engine. The engine was built by Ransomes of Ipswich, and tested at Aldershot, but found to be too heavy to satisfy either the designers or the War Office committee appointed to further the development of mechanical transport for military purposes.

In 1904 Hounsfield began work on his own on the development of a really cheap and economical motor car. A prototype was built in the period 1910–12 which had its curious duplex two-stroke engine mounted vertically between the seats. Mounted on solid tyres, the snub-nosed prototype embodied most of the un-orthodoxies which were to appear on production cars, though at that time Hounsfield had not the financial backing to begin quantity production. In 1914 he registered the company of Trojan Limited, precision engineers, of Croydon; five pre-production cars were built when the company's normal business programme allowed, but the real break-through came in 1922 when

Hounsfield sold the licence to manufacture to Leyland Motors, the firm of lorry builders who had just entered the car market with the Parry Thomas-designed Leyland Eight, the most expensive luxury car on the British market. This attempt to rival Rolls-Royce was doomed to failure, so Leyland was now aiming at the other end of the market.

On 24 June 1922, *The Autocar* carried the first description of the '10 hp two-stroke Trojan, a Small Utility Car, incorporating a Novel Two-stroke Engine, Epicyclic Gear, & Solid Tyres.'

'In producing the Trojan car,' they reported, 'the manufacturers, Messrs. Leyland Motors Limited, Ham Works, Kingston-on-Thames, have aimed at a simple utility vehicle of which a low operating cost should be a distinction. There is, of course, nothing new in designing for production at a low figure, but in the Trojan car this is carried to such an extent that there has been no hesitation in breaking away from tradition, as is evidenced by practically every component in the chassis. Briefly, the chassis may be described as a shallow metal

Below: looking rather like a boxer with a broken nose is this 1912 Trojan two-seater runabout prototype. It was powered by a small two-stroke engine

box, or tray, in and across which is mounted a novel two-stroke power unit and epicyclic gear, and at the corners of which are attached long semi-elliptic cantilever springs supported at their free ends on tubular axles.'

The most unusual feature of an already unorthodox design—'It's wierd, but it goes,' joked Hounsfield—was the engine, which was substantially that developed for the prototype but now mounted horizontally beneath the floor, leaving the cavernous interior of the bonnet almost empty save for the petrol tank, the steering column, and the carburetter, which lived in splendid isolation four feet away from the power unit.

The layout of the engine was unique: the four cylinders were arranged in a square, each pair of cylinders being united by a common combustion chamber incorporating a single sparking plug. The pistons were carried on a long V-shaped connecting rod, which, by virtue of its one piece of construction, varied the timing of the individual cylinders, of which the upper were the inlet and the lower the exhaust cylinders. But this posed further mechanical problems, for it was obviously impossible for the rod to travel its pre-destined path without bending; so Hounsfield made the connecting rods thin enough to flex slightly as they went about their business. He claimed that this equalised side thrust on the cylinder walls, minimising engine wear, and further pointed out that a single big-end bearing was far more mechanically correct than the articulated pattern normally used with V-shaped connecting rods.

Nevertheless, some trouble was experienced with the plain-bearing big-ends used on early production models, and so roller-bearing big-ends, more amenable to petroil lubrication, were standardised in 1923. The petroil mixture followed a tortuous path through the engine, having first to navigate a long inlet pipe, which was fitted with a 'small cylindrical chamber' to silence the carburetter hiss and, more importantly, to catch any blow-back of fuel when the engine, in its unhurried two-stroking, suffered the hiccups, as it was apt to do at certain speeds within its somewhat limited compass of some 1500 rpm. Then the petroil was sucked into the inlet cylinder below the piston, passed round the crankcase, where the compression stroke took place, separating oil from the fuel, was forced out through the transfer port into the upper cylinder, ignited and exhausted by the lower piston. The separated oil was caught in special chambers containing tiny plunger pumps actuated by the varying pressure in the crankcase and by a pipe linked to the exhaust, and thus fed to

Below: two views of the 1924 Trojan PB 10 hp model; the engine was a four-cylinder, two-stroke unit of 1529 cc; it had a two-speed epicyclic transmission and the car was fitted with solid tyres

the engine bearings. 'The system,' said *The Autocar* with justification, 'is novel and ingenious.'

Despite all the oil mist floating about in its interior, the engine was claimed never to need decarbonising or reboring; some owners claimed 100,000 miles between overhauls, which, judging by the dilapidated state of some of the Trojans still to be seen in everyday use on the roads in the 1950s, was very likely true. But as the average 1920s four-stroke light car engine needed decoking every 3000 miles or so, the performance of the Trojan on this count was not to be scorned.

As a speed car, however, it was a different story. The two-speed epicyclic transmission, was chosen for simplicity and the fact that the most idiotically unskilled driver could not fail to make a noiseless gearchange.

Below: a 1931 Trojan RE saloon in action; the RE model was introduced at the London Motor Show in 1929; it retained the four-cylinder duplex two-stroke engine, but featured a new three-speed epicyclic gearbox

This emphasis was bound to have some inhibiting effect on progression: the maximum power output of the 1529 cc engine was only 11 bhp, limiting the top speed to a little over 30 mph. The saving grace of the power unit, though, was the fact that it had a very flat power curve, developing 10 bhp at 400 rpm, 11 bhp at 900 rpm, and falling back to 10 bhp at 1200 rpm. Thus the Trojan could climb almost anything—albeit with the speed of a lethargic glacier—on its lowest speed, accompanied by an animal moaning from the bottom gear pinions and double-chain final drive.

The stolid respectability of its performance and its total lack of ostentation made the Trojan an ideal vehicle for clergymen—indeed the marque was the only one to advertise in the *Church Times*—who could thus grind about their business like the mills of God in an agreeable mixture of mechanical progress and haircloth austerity.

Economical running costs were another plus-factor in the Trojan's favour: 'Wasn't it cheap on petrol!' recalled a former Trojan owner to the author recently. 'You could get 50 to the gallon out of it easily . . . and it would climb anything. If a hill was too steep for bottom gear, you just turned around and went up in reverse. I recall that it had a big starting lever by the driver's seat—you pulled it up to start, just like a motor mower. But even with those long springs, the ride on those solid tyres was really hard—and if your tyres went down the tramlines, you had to drive all the way to the depot to get out again!'

Of course, the 'tram-line' story was purely apochryphal, part of the voluminous folk-lore which grew to surround the Trojan: for one thing the tyres were too wide; for another, the track was too narrow . . . And what is even more certain proof is that in 1925 three Oriental gentlemen drove a very secondhand

Right: in 1962, Trojan began building the Heinkel bubble car under licence as the Trojan 200; this, however, did not prove to be a very profitable venture

Above: in 1974, the Trojan name appeared on this Formula One Cosworth-Ford-engined car; the car was designed by former Brabham designer, Ron Tauranac and was driven by Tim Schenken of Australia. Unfortunately, lack of finance meant insufficient development and the team never enjoyed much success

Another unique feature was the rear number plate, made of a translucent material on which the registration was painted to allow the electric bulb of the rear lamp to also light up the numerals; 'pinholes in the fabric which covers the tail lamp recess, on the inside of the car, show the driver that the rear light is functioning properly.'

Shortly after the car's introduction, a 'detachable coupé top' became available at an extra cost of £40 (a not inconsiderable proportion of the original cost of £230 for the complete vehicle). By 1925 the price of the Trojan had fallen to £125, placing it on a par with the British-built Model T Ford which looked positively luxurious by comparison (but paid £23 in road tax each year against the £10 of the Trojan).

The economic virtues of the Trojan were not lost on the business community, who were keen users of Trojans for delivery purposes, perhaps the most famous being Brooke Bond Tea who had nearly 2,000 Trojans on the road in 1927. The Royal Air Force was another enthusiastic Trojan operator.

The success of the Trojan was greatly to the benefit of the Trojan Company who were still operating as precision engineers while receiving a royalty on each Trojan constructed by Leyland: peak output was 85 Trojans a week. In 1926 Trojan Limited became sole concessionaires for the marque they had created and a couple of years later took over manufacture.

By this time some civilising refinements had been made to the Trojan, such as the optional availability of pneumatic tyres; and the 1928 Trojan Achilles fabric saloon was little uglier than other enclosed light cars of the period. And, at £189, it was decidedly good value, despite its continued lack of front wheel brakes.

At the 1929 Motor Show a new Trojan, the RE Type made its début, with the engine carried in what appeared to be a luggage boot at the rear of the car. It retained the four-cylinder duplex engine of its predecessor, but had a three-speed epicyclic gearbox with gate gear change; the rigid rear axle had disappeared, to be replaced by a unit with a lockable differential. The standard tourer and saloon on this chassis both cost £179, while there was a deluxe model for £198 which had such un-Trojan features as an electric starter motor, wire wheels and an electric screen wiper; but there were still no front wheel brakes.

The original pattern of Trojan, mostly in light van form, continued in production alongside the RE Type, which had now lost all its old price advantage compared with more orthodox vehicles. It took a further five years for Trojan to make any attempt at a more modern design, which appeared on the eve of the 1935 Motor Show. This was the Mastra, which had a six-cylinder duplex two-stroke engine at the rear of the chassis driving through a conventional three-speed synchro-mesh gearbox. It was cloaked in up-to-the-minute streamlined coachwork by Ranelagh, which gave it an external appearance of conventionality, though on one prototype the effect was somewhat marred by the use of solid tyred disc wheels obviously borrowed from a superannuated 10 hp car. Advanced features of the specification included—at last—four-wheel-brakes, built-in hydraulic jacks and a heater. But at a price approaching £400, the Mastra was both too expensive and too unorthodox to appeal to the car buying public, and it never reached the production stage. Thereafter, Trojan concentrated on commercial vehicles until 1962, when they began building the already obsolete Heinkel bubble car under licence as the Trojan 200. Elva were also produced by Trojan, who absorbed the company in 1964. More recently, Trojan has increasingly been involved with motor racing, first building McLaren cars and later their own GP car.   DBW

Trojan from Singapore to London without once getting stuck in tramlines.

Braking was another curious feature of the Trojan: there was only one brake drum on the differential-less rear axle, and the handbrake (operated by a pull-up 'umbrella' handle) acted on a band wrapped round the bottom gear shaft, and was generally inoperative by virtue of being soaked with oil. It didn't matter, however: 'The reverse gear is employed as the second, or emergency brake,' cheerfully pointed out *The Autocar.*

The crowning eccentricity of the Trojan was its coachwork. On the original model this was a particularly uncouth chummy four-seater; *The Autocar* damned its shortcomings with the faintest of praise. 'As regards the bodywork, this may be described as an occasional four-seater, for although four adults may be carried with ease, the limitations imposed by wheelbase, and the special design of the chassis as regards springing, render the leg-room hardly sufficient for a long journey.'

Upholstery was deliberately kept to a minimum in anticipation of the unwholesome loads which might be carried in the vehicle. There were only two doors to the bodywork, with no apparent access to the rear seats. In fact, the front seat cushions were detachable, and the rear of the passenger's seat swivelled so that those short-limbed unfortunates destined to occupy the rear of the car could clamber through. Should the owner wish to carry pigs, poultry or garden produce in the rear of his vehicle, the rear seat cushions could be completely removed, and a special pattern of back panel which let down into a tail gate could be specified. The average Trojan owner was obviously expected to be a squirrel-like creature of hoarding habits, for, 'tool lockers are arranged under both the front seats, and under the rear seat is another large locker and two smaller lockers, while a large cupboard is formed in the instrument board and serves to house the side curtains, and at the same time provide room for small parcels.'

TOO MUCH TOO SOON

Preston Tucker was a frustrated genius whose advanced designs caused great consternation among the Detroit manufacturers

THE UNPRECEDENTED SELLERS MARKET in the American motor industry after World War II saw several new-comers attempting to break into the monopoly held by Ford, General Motors and Chrysler—the Big Three. None was more spectacular than the Tucker Corporation of Chicago. Preston T. Tucker, of Ypsilianti, Michigan, had previously been known as an associate of Harry Armenius Miller in the construction of a number of successful racing cars, including one which had set up many records on the Bonneville Salt Flats, including a top speed of 244 mph and an average of 150 mph for 500 miles. Now he intended to produce an entirely new type of passenger car, sporty, modern in appearance and completely radical in mechanical conception. It was to be rear-engined and equipped with automatic transmission, and independently suspended all round; at press conferences Tucker would pile up conventional axles and other components to demonstrate the amount of unnecessary weight he had designed out of the car. His plans for a sports car called the Torpedo were shelved, but in the spring of 1946 he began organising a company to produce a saloon car.

Tucker was a flamboyant character who believed in spending money while he wheeled and dealed. He was well connected in Washington, and secured a lease on a big aero-engine plant in Chicago where Dodge had been building power units for Boeing Superfortresses. It was claimed to be the largest factory under one roof in the world. The US Government was anxious to unload this plant, which had become a white elephant with the declaration of peace; it was also keen for cars to be built to meet the post-war demand. As soon as Preston Tucker had signed the agreement for his new venture, he sent his sales and engineering vice-president, Fred Rockelman (who had been one of the founders of Ford in 1903) straight back to Chicago on a chartered plane, which had been standing by in readiness during the negotiations; Rockelman's brief was to open offices in Chicago immediately.

Tremendous public and trade interest had been shown in the revolutionary concept of the Tucker automobile when details were announced in the press. Tucker intended to cash in on this enthusiasm to finance his venture, by selling dealerships before he began full-scale production. More than $8 million was raised from dealers anxious to sell the Tucker car, and a comprehensive sales network was organised, covering not only the United States but also export markets in 1800 retail outlets.

Tucker also raised capital by a conventional stock market issue: but this brought his company under the purview of the Securities Exchange Commission of the US Government, which insisted that all the un-orthodox features proposed in the prospectus of the new car should be fulfilled. This would doubtless have been fine under normal circumstances, but Tucker had no time to spare for development of the technicalities of the new car: it had to be right first time . . .

Tucker's power unit proposed problems: it was to be a flat-six, transversely mounted between the rear wheels, and driving a wheel from each end of the crankshaft through twin hydro-kinetic torque con-vertors to give a theoretically infinitely variable auto-matic transmission. Moreover, in the interests of engine flexibility, the conventional system of valve operation through a camshaft, tappets and push-rods was to be abandoned in favour of variable valve timing, actuated by an hydraulic pump and distributor. Unfortunately,

Below: only a handful of these Tucker 48 sedans were ever made; had the car ever gone into production, however, it would have been years ahead of its time (1948) as it had a number of features which were not even commonplace on some American cars of the 1970s. These features included an air-cooled engine, disc brakes, pop-out safety windscreen and an 'uncrushable' passenger compartment

Rockelman found that though the system was fine in theory, in practice the heat of the engine caused the hydraulic fluid pushing the valves open to expand, upsetting the valve timing and affecting performance. So a substitute power unit was found in the shape of a flat-six developed for a Bell helicopter, by Air-Cooled Motors of Syracuse, New York (successors to the Franklin motor company). Preston Tucker perversely had this unit converted to water-cooling . . . Nor was the Tuckermatic transmission a success, for it proved impossible to make it work in reverse. The company spent a great deal of money attempting to cure the problem, but nevertheless, when the prototype was demonstrated to the press, it had no reverse. The flamboyant Tucker was quick to counter press criticism of this minor shortcoming: 'Preston Tucker never backed up for any man!' he growled.

In order to get some demonstration vehicles on the road, a number of prototypes were built using modified Cord transmissions, with electrically-selected gears; other features of the original concept which were hurriedly abandoned were front cycle-type wings swivelling with the wheels and a central driving position.

Nevertheless, the styling of this 'compromise' car was so different from anything else on the roads of America that it created an immediate sensation. The work of former Auburn-Cord-Duesenberg stylist Alex Tremulis, the Tucker body was only 5 feet high on a 128-in wheelbase, very long and sleek, with a unique three-headlamp layout carried over from the abortive Torpedo sports car. Helping keep the height down was all-round independent suspension, by superimposed wishbones at the front, and at the rear by trailing arms sprung by rubber-in-torsion units, a concept exactly similar to that adopted for the original Issigonis Mini. Unfortunately, the art of bonding rubber to metal was still in its infancy, and the components of the rear suspension were liable to come unstuck at high speeds, leading to instability and, in one case, to the total destruction of the car.

'You'll step into a New Automotive Age when you drive your Tucker '48,' ran the company's slogan, and a reported 300,000 motorists placed orders for this revolutionary new car—which was, incidentally, the first of the safety-engineered saloons, with disc brakes, pop-out windscreen, padded dash and an 'uncrushable' passenger compartment.

But the company was still in difficulty with its development problems, still laboriously hand-building demonstration cars for the dealerships. They never did manage to get the Tuckermatic transmission to work properly: all the Tuckers which appeared on the road—and there were only 45 of these—had the modified Cord transmission.

More finance became necessary, and Tucker turned to the Government's Reconstruction Finance Committee for a $30 million dollar loan. With anticipated sales in excess of those for Studebaker or Buick, it seemed as though Tucker would experience no difficulty in raising the money: but now the grey men of the Securities Exchange Commission stepped forward, claiming that as the cars being offered to dealers differed materially from those described in the prospectus—most importantly in the substitution of a conventional type of transmission for the automatic—Tucker and his associates were committing a fraud.

So the loan was refused, and the Tucker company was forced into voluntary liquidation, though it was all geared up to sell everything it could produce, and had several million dollars in the bank.

A receivership was set up, and though a financial consortium from Texas was anxious to refloat the company and begin production, it was not permitted to do so. The final act was the indictment of Preston Tucker and five of his associates, including Rockelman, for fraud. After a long court session they were acquitted; but it was too late to save the company. Bureaucracy had won the day against mechanical innovation, and the Tucker Company died leaving only the legacy of the few hand-built prototypes and the memory of a car decades ahead of its time in engineering and performance, with many advanced design features which are not even commonplace on American cars of today.

In 1955, six years after his acquittal, Preston Tucker was once again back in the news. He announced plans to build a new Tucker car designed by Alexis de Sakhnoffsky. However, Tucker was unable to raise the considerable finance necessary and the project died with him.   DBW

Top left: the Tucker designer, Alex Tremulis, and his staff hard at work refining each detail of the Tucker sedan wooden model

Above left: the first Tucker engine was an enormous 589-cubic-inch unit and was situated crosswise on the overhang between the two independently sprung rear wheels

Above right: one of the features of the Tucker 48 sedan was a padded dashboard and a pop-out windscreen; in spite of all the safety features, however, the cockpit interior had a remarkably uncluttered look

IN SEARCH OF THE ULTIMATE

By means of a lot of care and hard work, it is possible to extract maximum performance from the engine of a motor car

TUNING AND MODIFICATION of a vehicle's power plant means increased performance and, very often, more economy. In the old days, a tuning wizard was portrayed as a man with a screwdriver, an oily rag, and a few spanners. After a bit of tinkering under the bonnet, adjusting the mixture and playing with the ignition the car would be 10 mph faster as if by some undefined magic. Unfortunately, the character was more imaginary than real. Even then, it required no little skill, and understanding to perform such a motoring miracle, and now, with engines far more complicated, equipment and technology of a much more complex nature are demanded of the aspiring mechanical wizard.

To the average man, tuning, or tune-up as it is called takes the form of checking points and plugs, replacing and gapping them as necessary. The service is complete for many when the carburettor is adjusted for a proper idle mixture. But, of course, this just scratches the surface of the art. If the engine components needed attention then the car will obviously go better, but what ignition and carburation settings are required? The service manual will give the settings for the *average* car off any production line, but this cannot take into account the great variation that exists among similar production cars. They differ because manufacturers employ broad production tolerances in the various parts in order to keep costs down to a realistic level. The objective is to produce parts only just accurately enough to do the job and yet still fit. A particular engine may have all the tolerances cumulatively combined to render the standard carburettor jetting less than ideal. Thus, it is often that re-jetting the carburettor could, and very often does, result in better performance. It is in an instance like this that modern technology proves itself. The device best suited to identify the ideal settings and generally trouble-shoot an engine is a rolling road dynamometer. It is an expensive piece of equipment but one which pays dividends in getting the best from an engine which to all intents and purposes is standard.

A rolling road dynamometer measures horsepower at the rear wheels, usually in conjunction with an electronic engine analyser which busily detects many common faults that would otherwise go unnoticed.

It becomes apparent that the modern day tuning wizard has, apart from his screwdriver, rag and spanners, a dynamometer and associated equipment to the value of many thousands of pounds. With this, all the ancillary equipment on the engine including carburettor, ignition, and so on can be set individually to suit the particular engine. Each item he changes may only make a very small difference to the power output of the machine, but the dynamometer is able to instantly indicate the direction (negative or positive) and degree to which each change influences performance.

Assuming that we start with a car which is exactly to factory specification, then just how much difference can a really good tune-up make? Take a simple thing like spark plugs; changing these spark plugs to a more suitable heat range can very often net the odd 1 or 2 hp. Breaker points are another area which can often stand improvement. Curing point bounce may benefit another couple of extra hp at the top end of the rpm range. Setting the ignition timing for maximum power very often see 3 or 4 hp, and re-calibrating the carburettor by swopping jets, emulsion tubes, air correctors or even needles in the case of constant depression type carburettors, can see a likewise increase. By the time you have found each individual increase, you have quite a big performance bonus, and usually better economy as well. A 10 per cent increase in hp is a commonplace gain, but with a good operator on the dynamometer, gains of twice that amount are not infrequent.

Above: a beautiful example of a 1000 cc Mini engine built by the author; equipped with gas-flowed head, special camshaft and twin-choke Dell' Orto carburettor it produced 85 bhp at 6800 rpm

Left: the correct distributor-points gap is important for maximum power, as any alteration of this gap leads automatically to an adjustment of the ignition-timing setting

Modifications are slightly different. Basically this is a case of altering the specification of an engine in an effort to get more hp. Naturally, after this has been done, it should be accompanied by a session on a rolling road dynamometer to make sure that everything that has been changed is being used to its best advantage by having the carburetter and ignition settings suitably matched.

Assuming that we are burning our mixture properly and that our mixture is, in fact, correct for the application, then all engine modifications are fundamentally aimed at achieving one particular thing, and that is to allow the engine a greater rate of air consumption. The amount of air an engine can consume is obviously directly related to its hp output, for the more air that goes in, the more fuel that can be burnt. When more air is packed into a cylinder, the increased explosive force of combustion is readily converted to extra power with each stroke of the piston. Another way to increase the power is to alter the number of power strokes in a given time. If two power strokes occur in the space of time allotted for only one previously, power will naturally increase. In fact it will have doubled in this case. Making an engine produce more power is really a case of trying to achieve both these ends. Increasing the breathing efficiency of each stroke of the engine, and trying to fit more power strokes into the cycle of the engine means more higher revs with more performance.

One of the most common things to concern oneself with in the search for power is the cylinder head. Modified cylinder heads are often termed 'gas-flowed' to indicate that they have been specially adapted to allow a greater flow of internal gases in and out of their relevant ports than in the head's standard form. Such modifications allow the engine to breath better—to consume more air.

Another common modification to cylinder heads

Right: a beautifully prepared works BMW 3.0 CSL, used with great success in the European Touring Car Championship of 1973

Below left: tracing engine deficiencies is made easier by the use of an electronic performance analyser such as this one

Below left: two Lancia cylinder heads, the nearer one having big valves and skimmed face

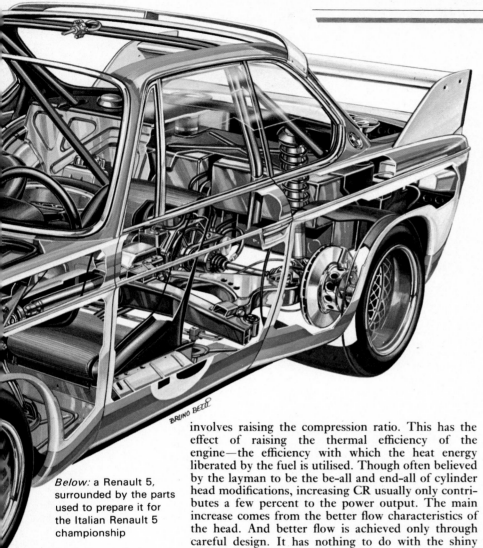

BRUNO BETTI

The fitting of a bigger carb or carbs, is equally popular in the pursuit of extra power. The idea is not necessarily to introduce more fuel to the engine, but once again, to force more air to the engine. Obviously, one carburettor supplying four cylinders presents a greater restriction on the air intake than four carburettors supplying four cylinders. The restrictive effect of a one carb system becomes more noticeable as revs rise. Accordingly, the fitting of a multi-carb system makes only a minor difference to power at low rpm, but a major improvement in the mid and upper rev ranges where a single carburettor may have been stifling the engine.

The carburettors used on an engine can be the most obvious sign of whether or not an engine has been modified for increased performance, hence the fact that insurance companies tend to load cars with multi-carburettor installations. For this reason, and the fact that carburettors are expensive, it's always best to see if you can achieve the hp you want without resorting to a carburettor change. In many cases this is possible, but some cars come equipped with such ridiculously small carburettors, that any increased hp without a carburettor change becomes impractical.

If gas-flowed big valve heads and sophisticated carburettor installations successfully allow the incoming charge easy access to the engine, then the next step is expelling the burnt charge from the engine. Most present-day exhaust manifolds are primarily designed

Below: a Renault 5, surrounded by the parts used to prepare it for the Italian Renault 5 championship

Right: two cylinder heads; the top one polished, the lower one with enlarged valves

involves raising the compression ratio. This has the effect of raising the thermal efficiency of the engine—the efficiency with which the heat energy liberated by the fuel is utilised. Though often believed by the layman to be the be-all and end-all of cylinder head modifications, increasing CR usually only contributes a few percent to the power output. The main increase comes from the better flow characteristics of the head. And better flow is achieved only through careful design. It has nothing to do with the shiny surfaces so reverently prepared by manufacturers to enhance sales potential—and profit margins. The only thing that really counts in a gas-flowed cylinder head is the shape of the ports and chambers.

with cost in mind. As a result, they are usually a simple, cast iron pipe connecting the cylinders. At low rpm this may be of no terrific disadvantage, but as soon as revs rise and with a concurrent increase in exhaust quantities, then the standard manifold can become the factor limiting decisive power output. The science involved in exhaust system design is quite complex, and although formulas have been devised which predict what dimensions should be used, we find that in practice, what goes on in the exhaust system is so complicated that the final design has to be done by a kind of trial and error on the engine test bed.

For a road-going system where silencers must be used, the biggest factor to overcome is to reduce exhaust back pressure to a minimum. The silencer, as well as damping out the noise produced by the engine, tends also to damp out the pressure fluctuations in the exhaust, which can often be used to aid exhaust extraction. On a racing system where no silencer is used, the situation is slightly different. Here these pressure pulses not only cause the scavenging of the combustion chamber when the piston is up around TDC, but also pull the incoming charge in, such that a fresh charge may start to come out of the exhaust valve even before the piston has started coming down on its induction stroke. It is the combination of shock-wave tuning and of the inlet and exhaust system on competition engines which can give volumetric efficiencies (that is the efficiency with which an engine will induce its fresh charge) of over 100 per cent.

Another item which comes in for some close attention when a lot more hp is required is the camshaft. The standard camshaft fitted to an engine is, of necessity, a compromise. It must be capable of giving a good spread of power and yet be quiet in operation. For a high performance engine, a cam with a longer opening period is often used. These sort of camshafts may well add power to the top end of the rev range, but do nothing for the bottom end of the rev range—the end most important for town driving.

With racing cams it really is a question of robbing Peter to pay Paul. The period of opening becomes so long that these cams give virtully no power under 4 or 5000 rpm. In other words, they start working where most road cams finish! A virtually intolerable situation for a road car, even a high performance road car.

Given the choice of methods of increasing hp output, the factory engineers will often go for increasing the capacity of an engine for numerous reasons. First of all, increased capacity gives you more power throughout the rev range and secondly, increasing the capacity of an engine at the factory is a pretty cheap way of getting more power. If you think about it, it must cost very little more to make a piston a bit larger and a crankshaft with a little longer stroke, especially if the original engine design allowed for such modification. Increasing the capacity, however, is not solely the prerogative of the factory engineers and many performance engine specialists follow this route as one of the items on their agenda for more hp. Unfortunately engine specialists cannot increase the capacity as cheaply as the factory because for them it may involve the use of special pistons to do the job, and in some cases, special crankshafts. These which are made in small numbers, are expensive.

Another method which used to be popular in the pre-war days and is now well on the road to recovery from a post-war slump, is supercharging, both the conventional supercharger and the exhaust driven turbocharger. Of all the forms of engine modification, supercharging sounds more potent, glamorous and exciting than the rest, due, no doubt, to some of the

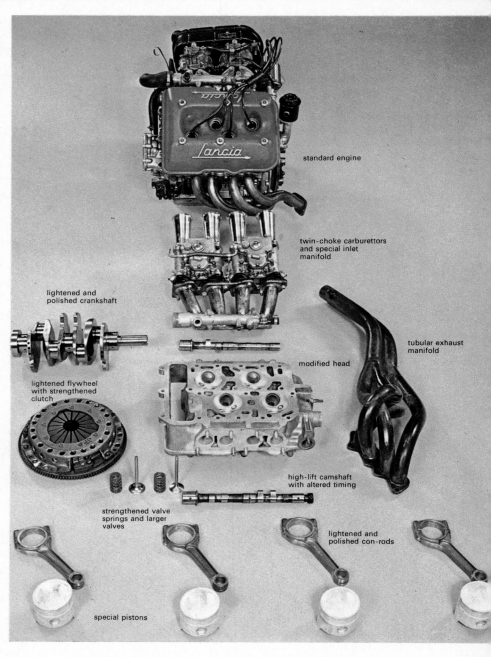

standard engine

twin-choke carburettors and special inlet manifold

lightened and polished crankshaft

tubular exhaust manifold

modified head

lightened flywheel with strengthened clutch

high-lift camshaft with altered timing

strengthened valve springs and larger valves

lightened and polished con-rods

special pistons

Above: the parts used by the Milan tuning firm of Baggioli to raise the power output of the 1600 cc Lancia V4 engine from 114 to 135 bhp

Left: a special camshaft can alter the power output of an engine considerably; here a high-lift shaft is shown alongside a standard item

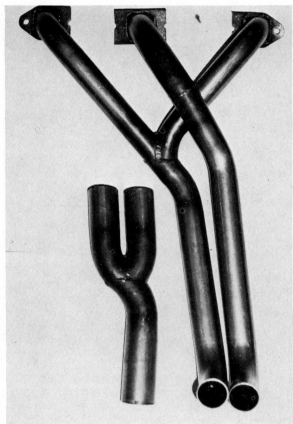

tremendous power outputs achieved by supercharged engines. When one considers that the average family saloon car engine puts out 40 or 50 hp, then outputs in excess of 1000 hp are bound to be somewhat awe-inspiring! Like most other forms of tuning though, supercharging does one thing, it allows the engine to have a higher air consumption, principally because it forces the air into the engine. The supercharger itself is nothing but a glorified pump but can easily account for an hp increase of between 50 and 200 per cent, depending on the application. You may well ask at this point if it's that effective, why car manufacturers don't use it as original equipment. It's quite simple—if a car manufacturer needs a 150 hp engine, it is easier to produce a 3-litre unsupercharged engine than a 2-litre supercharged one. In the first case he has only to make an engine; in the second he has to make an engine plus a supercharger. As pointed out before, capacity increase at the factory comes cheaply; the cost of a supercharger may be 25 times greater than the cost of increasing the capacity of an engine. Apart from that, living with a supercharger is not necessarily sweetness itself. A conventional engine-driven supercharger usually means increased fuel consumption simply from the fact that the engine is having to drive the supercharger all the time, whether or not the extra power is needed.

The exhaust driven turbocharger though is another kettle of fish. Correctly designed, the effect of a turbocharger on fuel consumption can be a lot less than a Roots or vane type, belt-driven supercharger. Apart from that, the exhaust driven supercharger has certain qualities which tend to keep the exhaust emissions down and this point in itself may find it favour amongst manufacturers, as present trends indicate. As well as this, the turbocharger is far more efficient as an air pump than a vane type supercharger, and in spite of requiring a more involved technology to produce it, it is usually more reliable. But even the turbocharger is not without its problems. Because of the fact that the intake turbine is driven via a shaft from an exhaust turbine, propelled by the exhaust, the supercharger has little effect at low rpm. It also suffers from what is popularly known as throttle lag, but should be more correctly termed boost lag. When the throttle is opened suddenly

Top left: a standard crankshaft alongside a lightened and polished version

Top centre: a comparison between standard polished pistons

Top right: standard and polished con-rods

Above left: a three-branch exhaust manifold to speed the gas flow from a Mini cylinder head

Above: supercharging can be a dramatically effective way of increasing output

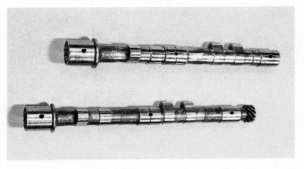

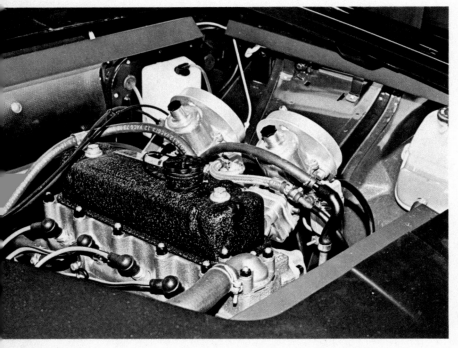

Confronted with such a wide variety of methods of increasing power, even quite a well-informed enthusiast can be forgiven for wondering which route to take for extra performance. It is difficult to give a hard and fast rule. Probably the first thing to do when considering how to gain extra performance is to divide all the tuning equipment into two categories; that which falls into the 'bolt on' category, and that which requires the engine to be removed in order to be implemented.

The bolt on category is, as would be expected, generally cheaper, but this equipment is also more limited. However, this need not be considered a great disadvantage, for in many cases, bolt on tuning equipment can still supply the extra performance that the driver requires. If bolt on performance equipment supplies the answer, then so well and good. If not, then the 'engine out' job must be considered so that more extensive engine surgery can be performed, such as a camshaft change or increasing the capacity by boring or stroking.

Once the route to increased performance has been chosen then the question is what to buy? not on a price per item basis, but on a price per hp gained basis. There are many modified cylinder heads on the market. One item might cost £25 and another £40. It could well be that the £40 one provides better value for money. If it produces a 10 hp increase, the extra performance is costing £4 per hp. The £25 modified head, on the other hand, may only produce a 5 hp increase, in which case it has cost £1 more per hp. But it doesn't end there. Just buying a cylinder head is only the beginning; numerous other factors must be included in the costing, such as gaskets and parts involved, time and labour charges, and lastly, and probably one of the most important steps, the cost of a run on a dynamometer must be considered to see that you are getting your money's worth of extra hp. Compare one firm's prices with another. Ask what sort of hp you can expect as a result of using certain items of a firm's equipment. All reputable firms will be only too glad to fully inform a genuine potential customer. Finally, remember you get what you pay for—quality always costs money.   DV

Top left: a much-lightened clutch

Top right: special valves and springs and camshafts are very useful

Above: a BLMC Special Tuning modified Midget

it takes a little time for the exhaust to speed up the turbine and thus give supercharge pressure. The turbocharged engine can thus be termed a soft engine and is best described to those who have never driven a turbocharged car, as having a slightly elastic throttle cable. In spite of its disadvantages, what it does for the hp of an engine is quite amazing and it almost boils down to how much hp is required, not how much hp is available. If the engine is strong enough to take the hp increase, the turbocharger will deliver.

FRENCH FAMILY FAVOURITE

Founded by two brothers-in-law, the Turcat-Méry company produced popular cars for European motoring enthusiasts

IN 1966, the man who was to be chief test pilot of the Concorde supersonic airliner drove from Paris to Moscow, a journey which, even in these days of rapid mass transit, still holds a flavour of romance. But what was truly remarkable about the journey of Olivier Turcat was that it was made at the wheel of a 58-year-old 18 cv Turcat-Méry limousine, built by his grandfather, Léon Turcat, in 1908.

Turcat and his brother-in-law, Simon Méry, had begun experimenting with Daimler-engined Panhard and Peugeot cars in the early 1890s in their home city of Marseille, before building a car of their own design in 1896. Their first experimental vehicle had a four-cylinder horizontal engine mounted at the front of the chassis, driving the rear wheels by chain; it also had pneumatic tyres, an advanced feature for the period. They first offered a car for sale in 1898–9, though their vertical four-cylinder Model A, with five forward speeds and two reverse gears, promised a rich crop of mechanical breakdowns for the unwary motorist.

By 1901, they were building on more conventional lines, following closely the design of the contemporary Panhard; they were also running short of cash. At this point, a fairy godfather in the portly guise of Adrien de Turckheim, arrived in Marseille on the advice of the motoring journalist, Paul Meyan: he was looking for a suitable design to be built by de Diétrich of Lunéville to replace the outdated Bollée models which they were currently producing.

A usefully flexible licence agreement was concluded by 1902, under which Turcat and Méry agreed to design for de Diétrich, while retaining their own motor factory in Marseille. The designs produced by the two firms were generally identical, though the Marseillaise vehicles seemed to have a slight edge on performance. This duplication of design proved especially useful, in the 1904 Gordon Bennett Eliminating Trials in which manufacturers were only permitted teams of three cars. De Diétrich and Turcat-Méry kept to the absolute letter of the rules by entering a team of three cars each—but it just so happened that the cars were of almost identical design, save that the rated horsepower of the Turcat-Méry cars was 100 while the de Diétrich entries were of 80 hp.

In the eliminating trials, the motor agent and racing driver Henri Rougier took third place on his Turcat Méry, which had already appeared in the 1903 Paris–Madrid Race finishing eleventh overall. Commented the Paris-based *International Motor Review*: 'The placing of the Turcat-Méry was undoubtedly a great surprise for the public, but it was not unexpected by those who know how much this clever Marseille firm have been perfecting their cars. Their presence in the team is not the result of a fluke, but is the reward for sound and conscientious work. Their success is further justified by the fact that Gabriel on his de Diétrich, which is constructed under Turcat-Méry licence, was only three minutes behind Rougier, and is therefore the

Below: Léon Turcat and his brother-in-law, Simon Méry, began experimenting with Daimler-engined Panhard and Peugeot cars in the early 1890s; by 1896, they had built their own car, the Turcat-Méry. Within a few years they had established themselves as manufacturers of interesting machinery. This is one of their giant pre-World War I Turcat-Méry tourers

first reserve. There has been a good deal of curiosity about the painting on the forepart of Rougier's car to represent some strange animal. The explanation is that Rougier comes from Tarascon which has been given a world wide celebrity by Alphonse Daudet, and he was tempted by the form of his motor bonnet to have painted on it the huge mouth and glaring eyes of the legendary beast of Tarascon, which is the principal figure in the annual carnivals. Rougier thinks that it will bring him good luck. We hope it will. But it will be interesting to know what the phlegmatic Teutons will think of this combination of medieval pictorial art with the modern automobile.'

In the race itself, Rougier was thought to have finished fourth, behind Théry (Richard-Brasier), Jenatzy (Mercédès) and De Caters (Mercédès), but following a protest Rougier was awarded an allowance of one minute which brought him into third place by just over twenty seconds on elapsed time. It was the last major race in which Turcat-Méry took part, though de Diétrich were still active in competitions.

On the touring car front, the Turcat-Méry-de Diétrich cars followed conventional lines, with chain final drive until 1908, shaft thereafter. There was, however, one splendid aberration in the shape of a six-wheeled touring car in which the front and rear wheels steered, while the centre wheels drove. Among the customers for this weird vehicle was the Khedive of Egypt; but perhaps the most flamboyant coachwork on this extraordinary chassis was that commissioned in 1908 by the Baron von Eckhardstein. Determined to outdo the luxurious Panhard Pullman *Limousine de Voyage* of his rival Count Boni de Castellane, von Eckhardstein spent £4000 on a Turcat-Méry-de Diétrich with stagecoach like coachwork with a passenger compartment furnished by Maple & Company and the rear of the body occupied by a fully equipped kitchen in which a chef could prepare gourmet meals while the car was in motion.

The dual personality of the Turcat-Méry lasted, it seems, until 1911, though the marque retained a similar design of radiator shell to what was now known as the Lorraine-Diétrich thereafter. In 1911 the range was extended and consisted of a 14 hp of 2614 cc, an 18 hp of

3308 cc and a 25 hp of 4084 cc.

That same year Turcat-Méry made its reappearance in competition, with a victory in the very first Monte Carlo Rally. Driver was once again Henri Rougier, who since 1909 had been mixing his career in motoring with a pioneering role in aviation. He was subsequently to win the Croix de Guerre and the Legion d'Honneur for his conduct in the First World War.

In 1912 two new models were added to the range, in the shape of a 28 hp of 4712 cc and a 35 hp of 6082 cc; an unusual feature of the largest model was a warning bell which rang if the oil pressure dropped to danger level. All the Turcat-Méry's were four-cylinders, a configuration from which the company only seems to have departed once in its history.

Production had always been small; and after the war it was apparent that the company lacked sufficient capital to operate successfully. Initially, the company produced a 3-litre 15/25 hp of conservative design, which failed to prevent a financial reorganisation of the company in 1921. Rougier was still racing for Turcat-Méry (though he was soon to join Voisin); in the 1921 Circuit de Corse, he came second, with other Turcat-Méry cars occupying third, fourth, fifth and sixth places. It was the last significant achievement of the marque in competition.

In 1923 a new model with a 2.8-litre ohc engine and four-wheel-braking was introduced, to be replaced twelve months later by a 2.4-litre ohc model, the UG Type. It was perhaps not entirely a coincidence that in 1924 Turcat-Méry underwent its second post-war financial reorganisation. Thereafter it was downhill all the way. From 1926 proprietory power units by CIME and SCAP were offered alongside the UG Type, and in 1927 there was even a straight-eight 2.3-litre SCAP-engined car. At that period, a small straight-eight was quite often the last desperate gambit of a dying company, and in 1928 Turcat-Méry ceased trading. Cars and spare parts were available from a company operating under the name Monnerot-Dumaine until 1933, but this operation, like the British firm of R. H. Collier, was merely an organisation existing on the sale of surplus cars and components remaining after a bankrupt motor manufacturer had shut up shop. DBW

Above: a 1925 Turcat-Méry 16/60 Pullman saloon. By 1925, the Turcat-Méry company was in trouble as it lacked sufficient capital to operate successfully. By 1928, Turcat-Méry ceased trading

A FARTHING A MILE

Turner cars were first powered by steam and were reputed to cost less than a farthing a mile to run

IT WAS IN 1896 THAT JULES MIESSE, of Brussels, built his first experimental steam car, which followed closely the layout of the contemporary Serpollet; two years later he began production, and by 1902 the three-cylinder single-acting Miesse steamer was being built under licence in Wolverhampton by Thomas Turner and Company.

At first trading under the name of the Miesse Steam Motor Syndicate, Turner claimed in 1902 that: 'Every portion of the Miesse Steam Car is constructed of the best English materials, and all the work is carried out at Wolverhampton. The engines and general mechanism are built with the greatest accuracy possible, consequently the cars run noiselessly and free from vibration.'

'Briefly,' ran the company's advertising, 'the advantages secured by the use of the Miesse System are: Instantaneous Generation of Steam; no boiler, hence no Danger of Explosion; Common Paraffin for fuel; Perfect Combustion, consequently Great Economy; Silent, and neither Smoke, Smell nor Exhaust Steam; Extreme Simplicity of Construction and Working enabling any novice to drive without possibility of injuring any part; Costs less than ONE FARTHING per mile for fuel; Speed up to 50 miles an hour, entirely at driver's discretion.'

The 1902 line-up consisted of 6 hp and 10 hp models; in 1903 a 20 hp was added; like the Serpollet, all had flash boilers. The three-cylinder engines were set transversely in the armoured wood chassis, with the cylinders horizontal.

By 1907, Miesse in Belgium had completely abandoned the production of steam cars in favour of a new petrol-engined model; but Turners of Wolverhampton continued to build steam cars of the original pattern until 1913. There was a brief flirtation with internal combustion in 1906, when a 20/25 hp petrol car was built for the London motor agents, Seymours Limited. It was a four-cylinder model of conventional design,

with a multiplate Hele-Shaw clutch and four-speed gearbox; it cost £450 in chassis form, £495 with touring coachwork and £600 as a landaulette. It was in production for only one year, after which Turner once again devoted themselves entirely to steam cars. Their 1908 range was augmented by a 30 hp model, in addition to the existing 10 hp and 16 hp; the new car cost £700 with side-entrance body, while the 10 hp in similar guise was priced at £450.

Just to confuse matters, Miesse were now represented in England quite independently from Turner-Meisse by the Miesse Petrol Car Syndicate, of Pelham Street, South Kensington, who offered a four-cylinder 24 hp model and a monobloc 35 hp six-cylinder at the 1907 Olympia motor show.

New Turner-Miesse models appeared at the 1908 Olympia Show; these were a light 10 hp model and a 12 hp model, both with shaft drive replacing the chains which had characterised earlier designs, though the chain-driven 15 hp and 20 hp were continued.

The first petrol car to be marketed under the Turner name appeared in 1910; it was a 9 hp Vee-twin cycle car with a curious two-speed gearbox which had a separate friction clutch for each ratio. Final drive was by shaft

Below: a 1904 Turner-Miesse tourer; these cars were designed by Jules Miesse of Brussels and built under licence in England by Thomas Turner and Company of Wolverhampton. The model was fitted with a three-cylinder steam engine set transversely in the armoured-wood chassis

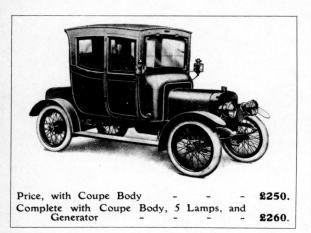

Price, with Coupe Body - - - **£250.**
Complete with Coupe Body, 5 Lamps, and
Generator - - - - **£260.**

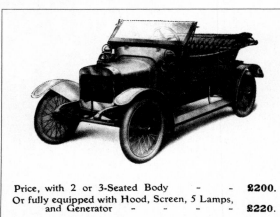

Price, with 2 or 3-Seated Body - - **£200.**
Or fully equipped with Hood, Screen, 5 Lamps,
and Generator - - - - **£220.**

Left: in 1913, Turner were marketing these two versions of the Turner Ten. By this time petrol engines had replaced the earlier steam engines and the two models, the standard sporting tourer and the closed coupé, were fitted with four-cylinder 1131 cc engines developing 10 hp

Left: a 1913 Turner 12 hp open tourer; it was powered by a four-cylinder engine of 1821 cc. A curious feature of the 12 hp was the use of fixed wire wheels with detachable rims; a spare rim was also included in the specification

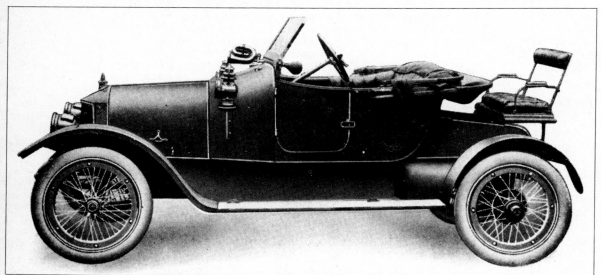

and worm, and, stated the makers, 'the whole of the axle casing revolves, on the ends of which the wheels are mounted; thus the weight of the car is carried on the axle-sleeves.' Price of the new car was £110.

At the 1911 Motor Show, the 8 hp model was uprated to 9 hp (and its price suitably upgraded to £165) and joined by two four-cylinder models, a 10 hp of similar appearance to the Vee-twin, save for its price tag of £197 to £222 (depending on the standard of finish of the bodywork), and a 15 hp, 2121 cc, priced at £365 with four-seated touring coachwork. By now, only the 15 hp steamer was being produced, and this was the last year the Turner-Miesse steam car appeared at Olympia.

The 1912 and 1913 Shows saw the Turner stand occupied by 1131 cc 10 hp fours and 1821 cc 12 hp models. The 10 hp could be specified in sporting form, with a four-speed gearbox instead of three-speed and a pointed radiator and streamlined coachwork, in which guise it retailed at £250 against the £200 of the standard model. A curious feature of the 12 hp was the use of fixed wire wheels with detachable rims; a spare rim was included in the specification.

Turner also built these cars for outside companies: there was the JB, a colonial version of the 10 hp marketed by John Birch & Company. There was also the Universal, based on 10 hp and 12 hp chassis.

This policy of manufacturing chassis for others to claim as their own was continued after the war, when Turners built the chassis for the Varley-Woods, a light car with a 1795 cc ohv Dorman engine; sponsors of this marque were Ernest Vernon Varley Grossmith, (of the

Grossmith family of soapmakers and actors), a failed mouth-organ maker and soup-canner, and John Woods, an East African river trader, who was eventually eaten by a lion at Lake Nyasa. But Varley-Woods failed to pay their bills, and Turner, who had exhibited only Varley-Woods chassis on their 1919 Motor Show Stand, were once again displaying under their own name at the 1921 Show—though the chassis exhibited seemed identical in specification to the Varley-Woods.

The 1922 range consisted of the 1795 cc 11/24 hp and the 2305 cc 14/30 hp; both models had worm final drive and four-speed gearboxes, and were priced in chassis form at £450 and £535 respectively.

Turner's last appearance at Olympia was in 1923, when only 12/20s were shown, in a down-rated specification with three forward speeds and spiral bevel final drive. A short-lived 2.1 litre Colonial model was introduced as running mate for the 14/30 (and eventually replaced it), but after 1926, only the 12/20 was built, in limited numbers, acquiring front-wheel-brakes as standard in 1928, somewhat behind its contemporaries. Within a couple of years, Turner had abandoned car manufacture altogether, but continued to market components of various sorts in later years.

Oddly enough, there was another Turner marque from Wolverhampton, built from 1951–1966 by Turner Sports Cars, who were in no way connected with the original Turner company. This latterday Turner featured glass-fibre bodywork on a tubular chassis, powered by a proprietary engine, usually by Ford or Coventry Climax. It was usually sold in kit form in Britain to avoid purchase tax.   DBW

GRAND TOURERS FROM BLACKPOOL

Life is never easy for the specialist sporting-car maker. Nevertheless, TVR challenged the odds with success

GREAT BRITAIN once had a wealth of small sports car manufacturers. In recent years the number has dwindled, due to the effects of legislation or lack of finance. The *marque* TVR, from Blackpool, has had a chequered career since the prototype was constructed in 1954. It had been managed by a succession of owners until the present proprietor, Martin Lilley, took control over 10 years ago. Lilley, unlike his predecessors, adopted a cautious approach, one which seemed to pay off.

The first TVR, built by Trevor (hence TreVoR) Wilkinson in 1954 at TVR Engineering of Blackpool, was a prototype road car. Basis was a tubular backbone-type chassis and power derived from a modified 1200 cc Austin A40 engine. The glassfibre body was a product of RGS Atlanta, a pioneer in this craft. The complete car weighed 14 cwt and Wilkinson hoped to put his machine into production.

A replica chassis was built for Ray Saidel, an American, who ordered six further examples. So TVR Engineering became a car manufacturing company. The year was 1956 and Wilkinson went into partnership with Bernard Williams, former dirt-track motorcycle star and director of nearby Grantura Plastics, and a production line established in a small factory. Two versions of the TVR were produced, a neat two-seater coupé or an open car which could be used in competitions. A developed version of the tubular backbone chassis was employed and TVR's own glassfibre body produced. Suspension was independent by means of Volkswagen-type laminated torsion bars and trailing arms. The power unit offered was either the twin-ohc 1098 cc Coventry Climax FWS or a Shorrocks-supercharged 1172 cc Ford 100E. The TVR's weight was quoted at 1400 lb with the Climax or 1450 lb with the Ford engine.

Every attempt was made to make the car as luxurious as possible, but it had its limitations. The suspension layout gave a high roll angle and to counteract this the springing was very stiff, resulting in a ride ideal for a race track but strictly 'vintage' for ordinary roads. Indeed, several successes were scored on the race track by Oliver and Stan Hart and Colin Escott.

In the United States Saidel and others won similar competition successes. The cars, known as Jomar Mk 2s, were fitted with the Climax engines, had several victories in 1958 at circuits such as Bridgehampton, Lime Rock and Thompson.

Inset: TVR Managing Director Martin Lilley stands outside the company factory in Blackpool, Lancashire

Below: the enthusiastic Managing Director had this special Roadster TVR constructed for his own use; it remained to be seen whether it would ever get into production

In 1957 the TVR was also available as a kit-car, thus saving customers the burden of purchase tax if they were willing to build it themselves. The following year production was increased to two cars per month, but this resulted in a financial problem which was eventually solved when a group of enthusiasts comprising Henry Moulds, David 'Bunty' Scott-Moncrieff, Irving Harris, David Hosking and Frank Lambert joined Wilkinson and Williams to form Layton Sports Car Ltd.

Production was increased and in 1959 the TVR Grantura Mk 2 was introduced. The coupé bodywork was revised, especially around the rear, and three engine variations were available: the Shorrocks-blown 100E Ford was offered in the Type F (quickly to be replaced by the new 997 cc Ford 105E), the 1216 cc Coventry Climax FWE in 83 bhp form in the Type C and the 1489 cc MGA unit in the Type M. When MG introduced the 1588 cc engine this was also made available in the TVR Mk 2A.

By 1961 disc brakes at last replaced the drum-type equipment which had been standard on all TVRs. The car continued to sell well, being a reasonably-priced individualistic machine ideally suited to motoring enthusiasts who enjoyed the machine's excellent handling and did not mind the harsh ride and somewhat cramped seating position. By now the firm's name had been changed to TVR Cars Ltd and the engine options were the MGA, now in 1622 cc form, and 1340 cc Ford Classic and, as always, the Coventry Climax FWE. Prices for the three models, in kit form, were £888, £795 and £1045 respectively, much cheaper than the Lotus Elite, for example.

More people became involved in the development of the car, among them motor trader Bryan Hopton, who became managing director, and Arnold Burton of the Montague Burton tailoring concern. Ex-Rolls Royce man John Thurner, who joined TVR to take control of the design and development side in 1958 (and who also raced the cars successfully), unveiled a totally new model at the April 1962 New York Motor Show. This was the TVR Mk 3 and it resulted in £1.5 million worth of orders for the Blackpool company. Thurner redesigned the suspension, employing a Triumph Herald-based wishbone and coil spring arrangement which, in turn, meant a new chassis. This was a much stiffer affair offering increased rigidity and although approximately 20 lb heavier than the Mk 2 there was a general reduction in unsprung weight thanks to the new type of suspension. Rack-and-pinion steering replaced the Ford 100E worm-and-peg system.

A separate competitions department was opened with ex-Triumph and BRM man Ken Richardson in charge. Sadly, TVR's attempts at prestigious long-distance sports car racing were a failure. In the Sebring 12-hours the three MGA-engined TVR Mk 3s battled merrily with the works-entered MGAs and Sunbeam Alpines until trouble intervened. The only finisher, following a long pit-stop to replace a steering arm, was Mark Donohue/Jay Signore in 25th place. The Le Mans 24-hours effort of Peter Bolton/Ninian Sanderson was a fiasco; they retired in the opening minutes after their vehicle lost all its water. In the Tourist Trophy at Goodwood Peter Bolton's car was an early retirement with a blown head gasket, while Keith Ballisat's finished eleventh overall and fifth in the 2-litre class. A three-car team of TVR Mk 2As was also entered in the Tulip Rally, the car of Arnold and S. H. Burton taking twentieth place overall and third in the 1600 cc class.

The competition programme was a severe drain on TVR's budget and once more they ran into financial

difficulties. In 1963 a new company, Grantura Engineering Ltd, was formed by Arnold Burton to take over production of the Mk 3 and soon the MGB-engined Mk 3 1800 was announced. There were rumours of two interesting projects, neither of which came to fruition. One was an MGB-engined open car with bodywork designed by Trevor Fiore, while the other concerned a unique engine, a three-cylinder, two-stroke motor designed by supercharger expert Keith Shorrock.

In the United States the history of TVR took on a new turn when a customer of an American firm, White Griffith Motors, complained about the delay in the delivery of a new MG engine for his TVR. Almost as a

Top: a row of TVR bodies, both 1600 and 3000 wait in the spray shop for finishing

Above: the abortive Tina, built by Fissore, on a Hillman Imp chassis, in 1966

Top: a Mk III Grantura 1800; this car was powered by the MGB unit

Above: posing outside the Fissore factory in Turin is the TVR Trident; the project was later taken on by Trident cars of Ipswich, after TVR themselves had shelved the idea of putting it into production

trim, heating, ventilation, brakes and suspension, resulting in a popular machine which came off the production line at the rate of four cars each week. The Ford V8-engined model was also still available to special order now known as the TVR 200 V8.

At the Turin Motor Show in November 1966 an exciting new venture was unveiled, the TVR Tina. This was basically a Sunbeam Imp Sport platform chassis plus mechanical parts mated by TVR to a Fiore-designed, Fissore-produced body. A very pretty car with obvious potential, it did not enter production. Such a machine required a volume of production which at that time TVR could not meet, while Chrysler could not guarantee the Imp would remain in production! After talks with Jensen about them producing the cars the project was shelved, only two prototypes being built.

Martin Lilley's recipe of walk-before-you-run, unheeded by previous owners of TVR, worked. The 1800 remained in production until the October 1967 Earl's Court Motor Show when the TVR Vixen superseded it. This was a tidied-up version of the 1800 using Ford's 1599 cc Cortina engine. A year later the TVR Vixen S2 was unveiled, this featuring a $4\frac{1}{2}$ in longer wheelbase and in 1970 the car was 'federalised' for the United States market, becoming the S3. Big-engined TVRs remained in production, the TVR Tuscan V8 replacing the 2000 V8 in 1967. In April 1969 another version of the Tuscan, using the 3-litre Ford V6 engine, was introduced. All three models, the Vixen, the Tuscan V6 and the Tuscan V8, shared the same chassis.

In 1971 TVR revealed a new range of Triumph-engined cars. Into the old body, which had been adapted to fit a new chassis, went the 1500 cc Triumph Spitfire engine, this model being namef the TVR 1300. The use of the six-cylinder $2\frac{1}{2}$-litre Triumph engine, as used in the TR6, resulted in the TVR 2500. The revised chassis, of round and square tubing, offered greater rigidity. Its *real* purpose was discovered in April 1972 with the introduction of the 'up-market' TVR M-series. A more luxurious model with a more up-to-date body style, the M-series was available in three forms: the 1600 M with the Ford engine, the 2500, with the Triumph engine (chiefly for export to the United States and Canada as the unit satisfied emission control regulations) and the 3000 M with the Ford V6 unit.

Eventually, in order to rationalise the range, the old-style bodywork was phased out. For a while, too, the 1600M was discontinued. At the onset of VAT, it was dropped, but early in 1975 it was reintroduced, selling at £2896 compared to £3256 for the 3000M.

In January 1975 the Blackpool-based firm had yet another setback in its chequered history. A fire, started by an electrical fault in a car, destroyed £80,000 worth of components, including a year's supply of pre-formed chassis tubing, and caused total damage estimated at £250,000. It took three months for production to be resumed, by June cars were being built at the rate of five per week.

With a sporting reputation, TVR cars continued to enjoy success in competition work over the years. Tommy Entwistle was one of the main TVR protagonists in the 1960's, winning the prestigious Fred W. Dixon production sports car championship in 1963. Gerry Marshall enjoyed many successes with a powerful V8-engined TVR 200 V8 in 1966, while John Akers and Mike Day found winning ways in autocross, Day becoming British Champion in 1969 and 1970. In 1970 Rod Longton won the STP Production Sports Car Championship in a 3-litre TVR Tuscan V6, while the similar machine of the late Brian Hough repeated the dose in 1971 and 1972. MK

joke the firm lowered in a Ford V8 engine—and it fitted! The result, after surprisingly little strengthening of the chassis or running-gear, was the TVR Griffith 200. An arrangement was made to ship engineless cars to the United States where either the 195 or 271 bhp versions of the 4727 cc Ford V8 engine were installed and the car sold for $3900—$2100 less than the similar concept, the AC Cobra, a car the TVR also outperformed.

Early in 1965 the popular 'fast-back' rear-end styling was applied to the TVR, rejuvenating the design. Next surprise was the TVR Trident, which featured up-to-the-minute styling thanks to a body designed by British stylist Trevor Fiore (at that time based in Paris) and constructed by Fissore of Turin. It was built in aluminium and fitted to a long-wheelbase version of the TVR chassis. Unfortunately, in August of that year TVR Cars Ltd went into liquidation, and the car was next seen as the product of a different company, Trident Cars Ltd, which survived until 1974 with the same basic body design but utilising Austin-Healey or Triumph chassis and running gear.

TVR Engineering Ltd took over the assets of the old firm in November 1965 under the direction of enthusiast Martin Lilley and his father, Arthur. The MGB-engined TVR 1800 Mk 3 remained in production until it was redeveloped as the Mk 4 midway in 1966. The engine was moved slightly forward in the chassis to facilitate access as well as improving the weight distribution, while attention was also paid to the

1600M/3000M

The TVR story began in Blackpool, Lancashire in 1954, and ever since the company has been building their own highly distinctive brand of sports car.

Amazingly, the TVR in its present form dates back to the 1956 car, but the company has kept the car looking as least as modern as any of its competitors.

The TVR is available with a choice of two engines: the Ford Cortina 1600 unit gives the car a top speed of 110 mph, and the even more powerful three-litre Ford Capri engine, that propels the one-ton car to a top speed of 125 mph. Due to public demand over the years, the company has introduced a 'hatch-back' version with their unique rear window hinged, so that access is exceptionally easy to the luggage compartment.

The car's glassfibre body is painted with as many coats of paint as the sprayer thinks is necessary for the car to be 'perfect'. It sits, unstressed, on a massive tubular backbone chassis with outriggers. The engine, either of the Fords, or the 2500TC Triumph engine, for the United States, nestles well back in the chassis, thus helping weight distribution and, consequently, the handling.

Entering a TVR, one gets the feeling that it is a typically English sports car, and as one drives along, your body can hardly forget that with a typically English sports car, one gets a typically English hard ride.

Those people wondering whether the company producing up to nine vehicles per week, takes time to make sure every one is road-worthy, may be cheered to know that not only is each car thoroughly tried by the works tester, but the Managing Director, Martin Lilley, personally tests many of the cars himself, just to make sure TVR's high standards are being maintained.

ENGINE Front-mounted, water-cooled 60° V6, or straight-four. 94 mm (3.70 in) bore × 72.4 mm (2.85 in) stroke = 2994 cc (182.7 cu in) (3000M), or 81 mm (3.19 in) bore × 77.6 mm (3.06 in) stroke = 1599 cc (97.7 cu in) (1600M). Maximum power (DIN) 142 bhp at 5000 rpm (3000M), or 86 bhp at 5500 rpm (1600M); maximum torque (DIN) 172 lb ft at 3000 rpm (3000M), or 92 lb ft at 4000 rpm (1600M). Cast-iron cylinder block and head(s). Compression ratio 8.9:1 (3000M), or 9.2:1 (1600M). 4 main bearings (3000M), or 5 main bearings (1600M). 2 valves per cylinder operated, via pushrods and rockers, by a single camshaft at the centre of the V (3000M), or side (1600M). 1 Weber downdraught twin-choke carburettor.

TRANSMISSION Single-dry-plate clutch and 4-speed manual gearbox. Ratios for 3000M (1600M in brackets) 1st 3.160 (2.972), 2nd 1.950 (2.010), 3rd 1.410 (1.397), 4th 1 (1), rev 3.350:1 (3.876:1). Hypoid-bevel final drive. Ratio 3.450 (3.770).

CHASSIS Tubular backbone with outriggers.

SUSPENSION Front—independent by wishbones, coil springs, an anti-roll bar and telescopic dampers, rear—independent by wishbones, coil springs and telescopic dampers.

STEERING Rack and pinion. Turns from lock to lock 4.2.

BRAKES Servo-assisted front discs and rear drums.

WHEELS 6 in × 14 in light-alloy.

TYRES 185HR × 14.

DIMENSIONS AND WEIGHT Wheelbase 90 in; track—front and rear 53.75 in; length 164 in; width 64 in; height 47 in; ground clearance 5 in; dry weight 2170 lb (3000M), or approximately 2000 lb (1600M); turning circle between walls 36 ft; fuel tank capacity 15 gals.

BODY Sports 2-door, 2-seater. Hatch-back opening third door, optional.

PERFORMANCE Maximum speed 125 mph (3000M), or 110 mph (1600M). Acceleration 0–60 mph 7.5 secs (3000M), or 8.8 secs (1600M). Fuel consumption 25 mpg (3000M), or 30 mpg (1600M).

This magnificent four-color encyclopedia is brought to you by Columbia House
in cooperation with Orbis Publishing Ltd., one of Great Britain's most enterprising publishers.
Rather than change any of the encylopedia's authoritative international automotive text, we have
included a glossary of terms that will give you immediate American equivalents, a conversion table
for the international metric system, and a conversion table for equivalent monetary values.

Glossary

BRITISH	AMERICAN	BRITISH	AMERICAN
Aerial	Antenna	Motor	Engine
Aluminium	Aluminum	Number plate	License plate
Apron	Skirt	Overrider	Bumper guard
Big-end	Rod (conrod) bearing	Paraffin	Kerosene
Blower *(colloquial)*	Supercharger	Parking brake	Parking lock
Bonnet	Hood	Petrol	Gasoline, "gas"
Boot	Trunk	Petrol pump	Gasoline or fuel pump
Brake servo	Power brake	Production car	Stock car
Bulkhead	Firewall	Propeller shaft	Drive shaft
Capacity	Displacement	Quarter light	Door vent
Carburetter; carburettor	Carburetor		
Check strap	Door stop	Rear lamp	Tail light
Clutch release bearing	Clutch throwout bearing	Rear seat squab	Rear setback or backrest
Control box	Voltage regulator	Reverse lamp	Back up light
Crown wheel and pinion	Ring gear and pinion	Roof lamp	Dome light
Cylinder block	Cylinder crankcase	Saloon	Sedan
Dip switch	Dimmer switch	Scuttle	Cowl
Door pillar	Door post	Selector rod	Shift bar
Drop arm	Pitman arm	Servo-assisted	Power assisted
Drop-head	Convertible	Side lamp	Parking light
Dynamo	Generator	Side member	Side rail
Epicylic gearbox	Planetary gearbox	Spanner	Wrench
Exhaust silencer	Muffler	Sparking plug	Spark plug
		Starting handle	Crank handle
Facia panel	Dashboard	Steering column	Steering post
Gear lever	Gear shift lever	Steering relay	Steering idler
Gearbox	Transmission	Stub axle	Steering knuckle
Gearbox housing	Transmission casing	Sump	Pan
Gearchange	Gearshift	Swivel pin	King pin
Glassfibre	Fiberglass	Toe board	Toe pan
Grease nipple	Grease fitting	Track	Tread
Gudgeon pin	Piston or wrist pin	Track rod	Tie bar or track bar
Half shaft	Axle shaft	Two-stroke	Two-cycle
Handbrake	Parking brake	Tyre	Tire
Hose clip	Hose clamp	Valance	Rocker panel
Ignition harness	Ignition set	Wheel arch	Wheelhouse or housing
Kerb	Curb	Wheel brace	Wheel wrench
		Windscreen	Windshield
Layshaft	Counter shaft	Wing	Fender
Main shaft	Output shaft	Wishbone	A-arm; Control arm
Marque	Brand, make	Works	Plant, factory

Metric Equivalents
(Based on National Bureau of Standards)

Length

Centimeter (Cm.)	= 0.3937 in.	In.	= 2.5400 cm.
Meter (M.)	= 3.2808 ft.	Ft.	= 0.3048 m.
Meter	= 1.0936 yd.	Yd.	= 0.9144 m.
Kilometer (Km.)	= 0.6214 mile	Mile	= 1.6093 km.

Area

Sq. cm.	= 0.1550 sq. in.	Sq. in.	= 6.4516 sq. cm.
Sq. m.	= 10.7639 sq. ft.	Sq. ft.	= 0.0929 sq. m.
Sq. m.	= 1.1960 sq. yd.	Sq. yd.	= 0.8361 sq. m.
Hectare	= 2.4710 acres	Acre	= 0.4047 hectar
Sq. km.	= 0.3861 sq. mile	Sq. mile	= 2.5900 sq. km.

Volume

Cu. cm.	= 0.0610 cu. in.	Cu. in.	= 16.3872 cu. cm.
Cu. m.	= 35.3145 cu. ft.	Cu. ft.	= 0.0283 cu. m.
Cu. m.	= 1.3079 cu. yd.	Cu. yd.	= 0.7646 cu. m.

Capacity

Liter	= 61.0250 cu. in.	Cu. in.	= 0.0164 liter
Liter	= 0.0353 cu. ft.	Cu. ft.	= 28.3162 liters
Liter	= 0.2642 gal. (U.S.)	Gal.	= 3.7853 liters
Liter	= 0.0284 bu. (U.S.)	Bu.	= 35.2383 liters

Liter = $\begin{cases} 1000.027 \text{ cu. cm.} \\ 1.0567 \text{ qt. (liquid) or } 0.9081 \text{ qt. (dry)} \\ 2.2046 \text{ lb. of pure water at } 4°C = 1 \text{ kg.} \end{cases}$

Weight

Gram. (Gm.)	= 15.4324 grains	Grain	= 0.0648 gm.
Gram	= 0.0353 oz.	Oz.	= 28.3495 gm.
Kilogram (Kg.)	= 2.2046 lb.	Lb.	= 0.4536 kg.
Kg.	= 0.0011 ton (sht.)	Ton (sht.)	= 907.1848 kg.
Ton (met.)	= 1.1023 ton (sht.)	Ton (sht.)	= 0.9072 ton (met.)
Ton (met.)	= 0.9842 ton (lg.)	Ton (lg.)	= 1.0160 ton (met.)

Pressure

1 kg. per sq. cm.	= 14.223 lb. per sq. in.
1 lb. per sq. in.	= 0.0703 kg. per sq. cm.
1 kg. per sq. m.	= 0.2048 lb. per sq. ft.
1 lb. per sq. ft.	= 4.8824 kg. per sq. m.
1 kg. per sq. cm.	= 0.9678 normal atmosphere

1 normal atmosphere = $\begin{cases} 1.0332 \text{ kg. per sq. cm.} \\ 1.0133 \text{ bars} \\ 14.696 \text{ lb. per sq. in.} \end{cases}$

Approximate Values of the Pound (£)
in terms of U.S. Dollars ($)

1914-1919	$4.76
1935	4.90
1936	4.97
1937	4.94
1938	4.89
1939	4.46
1940-1949	4.03
1950-1967	2.80
1968-1970	2.40
1971-1972	$2.40/2.60
1972-Present	2.60/2.10